MW00637887

Grammar Galaxy

Adventures in Language Arts

Supernova

Melanie Wilson, Ph.D.

Rebecca Mueller, Illustrator

GRAMMAR GALAXY: SUPERNOVA
Copyright © 2022 by Fun to Learn Books

All rights reserved. No part of this book may be reproduced or transmitted in any other form or by any means without written permission from the author: grammargalaxybooks@gmail.com.

ISBN: 978-1-7354939-4-7

Table of Contents

A Note to Teachers

I'm passionate about language arts. I love to read, write, and speak. As a homeschooling mom, I wanted my children and my friends' children to share my passion. Over the years, I found aspects of many different curricula that clicked with my students. But I never found something that did everything I wanted a complete curriculum for elementary and middle school students to do:

- Use the most powerful medium to teach language arts: story
- Give the why of language arts to motivate students
- Teach to mastery rather than drill the same concepts year after year

I felt called to create my own fast, easy, and fun curriculum for teachers who want to see students succeed in language arts.

Grammar Galaxy: Supernova is for students who have mastered the concepts taught in *Grammar Galaxy: Nova*. It is intended for both independent reading and as a read-aloud for a family or classroom.

When reading aloud, share the synonyms for vocabulary words given in the text. Following each story, there are questions to ask students to check for comprehension. The answers are given in the Appendix.

Students should complete the corresponding mission in the *Mission Manual* before moving on to the next story. Classroom teachers may wish to create customized missions.

I hope your students will accept the call to be guardians of Grammar Galaxy.

Melanie Wilson

P.S. I call typos Gremlins. If you or your student finds one, check the list at FunToLearnBooks.com/Gremlins. If it is not listed, contact me at grammargalaxybooks@gmail.com so I can make the correction.

A Note to Students

I need your help. Grammar Galaxy is in trouble. The Gremlin is working hard to keep kids from reading, learning new words, and spelling correctly. He also wants to keep them from writing and public speaking. He knows that if he succeeds, the English language will be weak, and life will be miserable.

Here is how you can help defeat the Gremlin. First, read each chapter in the text, paying attention to the vocabulary words that are in **bold text**. Note the synonym (word with similar meaning) that is given for each. Then make sure you can answer the discussion questions at the end of each chapter. If you can't, review the text, and if you still need help, check the Appendix at the back of the book. Finally, complete the mission in your mission manual with the same number as the chapter in this book.

I'm proud to have you join us as a guardian of the galaxy!

Melanie Wilson

Prologue

The king of Grammar Galaxy tried not to worry. He had made his three children, Kirk, Luke, and Ellen English, guardians of the galaxy. Together with the other young guardians on planet English, they had defeated the Gremlin and saved the English language many, many times. Words and punctuation marks were returned to their planetary homes, destructive laws were changed, and the kids had learned a lot about literature, grammar, and writing.

But would the Gremlin's schemes finally get the best of them? Would they eventually face a crisis they couldn't overcome with the help of *The Guide to Grammar Galaxy*? He didn't know. He asked Screen for a status report on the galaxy. All seemed well for the moment.

Unit I: Adventures in Literature

The Groaner

King Issues Law Requiring Kids to Read His Biography Daily

Chapter 1

The king was reading his paper at the breakfast table and smiled. "I can't believe it!" he cried.

"There is actually good news, or there are no grammar errors?" the queen quipped in response to the king's positive reaction.

"No. Better. *The Groaner* has been **deemed** misinformation. It's been shut down."

"Shut down by whom?" the queen asked.

"I don't know. Some truth-in-journalism nonprofit."

"And you're happy about this?" the queen asked disparagingly.

★ ★ ★ ★ ★ ★ ★ ★ ★

deemed – *regarded*

egregious – *outrageous*

carped – *complained*

★ ★ ★ ★ ★ ★ ★ ★ ★

"Of course I am!" the king said, raising his voice. "Why, it's as though you want those people to keep printing lies about me."

"Lies?" the queen said, frowning.

"Lies," the king insisted. "**Egregious** lies."

"Are they printing lies when it's funny?" she asked, smirking.

"Funny? You can't possibly think what they've written about me is funny," the king **carped**.

The queen walked away and returned with a copy of *The Groaner*. The king was pictured on the front page of the paper, handing a book to a child. The headline read "King Issues Law Requiring Kids to Read His Biography Daily."

"This is funny," she said, giggling.

"There are people who still think I made that law," the king grumbled.

The queen paged through the paper. "Look at this headline. 'Poll: Majority of Citizens Support Sending Gremlin to Planet Recycling.' You aren't the only one *The Groaner* makes fun of."

"Let me see that," the king said, reaching for the paper. He paged through and read another headline that made him belly laugh: "In Threat to the Guardians, Gremlin Reveals He Has Obtained the Darksaber."

"I don't understand that one," the queen said after he read it to her.

"The Darksaber is a powerful weapon in the space movies the kids and I watch," the king explained.

"Oh," the queen said, still not understanding the humor.

The royal children arrived in the dining room while they were talking.

"Listen to this one," the king said. "'King Is Building Another Castle to House Princess Ellen's Wardrobe.'" He laughed heartily, but Ellen didn't join him.

"What? Are you really building another castle?" Ellen asked.

"No, of course I'm not. They're just saying you have a lot of clothes," he explained, still chuckling.

"I don't have that many clothes," Ellen objected.

When the king didn't agree with her, she asked for the paper. She began paging through it and declared it misinformation. "They shouldn't be able to print lies about me. Can we sue them?"

"Don't worry, Ellen. The paper has been shut down, right, dear?" the queen said to prompt the king to reconsider.

"Yes, that is true," he admitted with a sigh. "Let's have breakfast and then we'll talk about what we should do."

After breakfast, the king led his children to the castle library. "*The Groaner* is satire," he said. "I want to remind you about satire by reading from *The Guide to Grammar Galaxy*."

Satire

Satire is the use of humor, irony, or exaggeration to poke fun in a good-natured way. It can also be used to criticize policies, leaders, or organizations. Satire is used by websites, cartoonists, and some talk show hosts. Sometimes satire is not recognized as such, causing the spread of misinformation and sometimes outrage. Less confusion results when social-media sites label articles as satire.

A **parody** is satire in the form of imitation. For example, the book *Goodnight iPad* by Ann Droyd is a parody of *Goodnight Moon* by Margaret Wise Brown. It pokes fun at our love of modern technology.

Diminution is satire that makes something seem smaller than it is in size or importance. Describing political leaders as children fighting is an example of diminution.

Inflation is exaggerating or enlarging something so that it seems ridiculous. A politician who has a noticeable nose will have an enormous nose in a satirical cartoon.

Juxtaposition is placing items together as though they are of equal importance when they are not. For example: *What I look for as a movie critic is believable character development, a unique plot, and well-buttered popcorn.*

"Even the guidebook says that satire can lead to the spread of misinformation. I'm glad *The Groaner* is being discontinued," Ellen said with a humph.

"Hm," the king said, stroking his beard.

11

"What are you thinking?" Luke asked him.

"I was glad the paper was being shut down, too," the king said slowly.

"But now you're not?" Kirk asked.

Before he could reply, Ellen reminded him that the paper printed misinformation about him, too.

"Yes, it did, Ellen. I don't like being made fun of any more than you do. But what I really dislike is censorship," the king said. He looked up another article in the guidebook and read it aloud to them.

Censorship

Censorship is when an authority eliminates, punishes, or hides communication it does not approve of. Censorship may be undertaken to protect an audience from exposure to misinformation, hate speech, mature content, violence, and immorality.

But censorship may also be used to protect the agency doing the censoring. Governments may censor to protect national security; corporations may censor to protect profits; and individuals may censor to protect reputations.

Book banning and social-media restrictions are examples of controversial censorship. Despite laws protecting speech, citizens' desire for both freedom and safety will continue to come into conflict over censorship.

"If you don't like misinformation or censorship, what are you going to do about *The Groaner*?" Ellen asked her father.

"*The Groaner* is satire, not misinformation. I have a feeling the Gremlin had something to do with shutting it down. I think you three can fix it."

"What do you mean?" Kirk asked.

"I would like you three to send out a mission on satire and censorship. Our young people can demand that *The Groaner* resume publishing."

"Hm. Before we do that, can I ask them not to make fun of me anymore?" Ellen said.

"Isn't that censorship, though?" Luke asked.

"It is indeed," the king replied. "Ellen, being a public figure means you'll be teased. The good thing is it keeps us humble."

Ellen sighed. "Okay. We'll send out a mission. But then I'm going to declutter my clothes. Can't have you building a whole new castle for them, Father."

They all laughed.

What does *egregious* mean?

What is censorship?

Why would the Gremlin want to shut down *The Groaner*?

Chapter 2

The queen was perusing social media in the afternoon and was pleased to see a funny headline from *The Groaner*: "*The Grammar Gazette* Purchases Industrial Washing Machines to **Spin** the News." She was surprised to see a notice under the article: "Rated false by our independent fact checkers. Click to read why." The queen clicked and read that the galaxy's newspaper had not purchased large washing machines and didn't use them to spin their newspapers. "Don't they know that the headline is satire?" she said aloud. "Strange."

★ ★ ★ ★ ★ ★ ★ ★ ★

spin – *misrepresent*

bias – *favoritism*

★ ★ ★ ★ ★ ★ ★ ★ ★

The queen returned to scrolling social media posts when another post got her attention. "Guardian Program Produces Improved Test Scores." She smiled and said aloud, "Of course it does!" But under this headline was another fact-checking notice. The queen clicked to read why the fact checkers rated it false.

"No randomly controlled trial was conducted to determine whether improved test scores are the result of the Guardian Program. There is no evidence to date that supports this claim. We rate it as false," the statement read.

"Who are these people and what's a randomly controlled trial?" the queen wondered aloud. At the bottom of the statement, the queen found the answer to one of her questions. A group called Citizen Fact Checkers had written the statement.

A quick Internet search produced the answer to her second question. "A randomly controlled trial is an experimental model in which subjects are arbitrarily assigned to an experimental (treatment) or control (no treatment) group. This assignment avoids selection **bias**. In a double-blind study, neither the subjects nor experimenters know who is in the experimental group. This study design is desirable as it avoids **unwitting** influence of the results."

★ ★ ★ ★ ★ ★ ★ ★ ★

unwitting – *unknowing*

★ ★ ★ ★ ★ ★ ★ ★ ★

The queen thought she understood what the Citizen Fact Checkers were saying. The guardians hadn't been randomly assigned to the program. And of course, everyone knew who was in the program. There was no way to be sure that it was the Guardian Program that had produced better test results.

At dinner that evening, the king began boasting about the galaxy's test scores. "Our Guardian Program has improved test scores significantly. You children should be proud of what you've accomplished."

The children smiled, but the queen frowned.

"What is it, dear?" the king asked his wife. "You don't want them to be proud? How about happy then?" he suggested cheerfully.

"It's not that," the queen said. "It's just...the independent fact checkers rated that as false. The Guardian Program isn't responsible for our test scores."

The king was stunned and said nothing for a moment. "If the guardians aren't responsible for better test scores, who is?" he asked quietly.

"I don't know."

The king's face reddened in anger. "You just know it isn't the Guardian Program."

"Right," the queen replied quietly.

"Who are these fact checkers that you're listening to?" the king asked sternly.

"They are Citizen Fact Checkers."

"And you trust them," the king said with a disapproving tone.

"I learned about randomly controlled trials from them. And the test scores were not produced in a double-blind study," the queen said indignantly.

"Let me get this straight," the king said. "Because the test scores weren't from a double-blind study, the guardians don't deserve any credit?"

The queen ignored the king's anger and replied, "Yes."

The king excused himself abruptly and stormed off.

The children looked uncomfortably down at their plates. They finished their meal in silence and gathered in the media room.

"What just happened?" Luke asked his brother and sister.

"Father got mad at Mother for questioning him," Ellen declared.

"I don't think that's the only thing," Kirk said.

"What do you mean?" Ellen asked.

"I've heard about fact checkers causing a lot of conflict online," Kirk explained. "What group did Mother mention?"

"Citizen Fact Checkers I think," Ellen said.

"Okay. Screen," Kirk ordered, "give me background on the group Citizen Fact Checkers."

Screen complied and soon reported that Citizen Fact Checkers was a new group with an unknown backer. It had been caught fact-checking satire and appeared to have an anti-galaxy bias. They consistently rated positive news stories about the king, the guardians, and the English language as false. They also rated negative stories about the Gremlin and poor language-arts skills as false. The group's fact-checking had resulted in angry comments on social media, Screen said.

"It's resulted in angry comments here, too," Ellen said sadly.

"If the fact checkers aren't telling the truth, how are we supposed to know what's true?" Luke asked.

"I wonder if there is an article on fact-checking in *The Guide to Grammar Galaxy*," Kirk said.

The children looked at one another and made their way to the castle library to see. Kirk checked the table of contents and found what he was looking for. He read the article aloud.

Fact-Checking

Investigation of non-fiction material to verify claims is called fact-checking. Social media has replaced journalists as the sole fact checkers. To prevent the spread of misinformation, students must do their own fact-checking.

To begin fact-checking, distinguish between fact and opinion. Facts can be proven or disproven with evidence. Opinions are beliefs that don't rely on evidence. "My mom is 47" is a statement that can be fact-checked with a birth certificate. "My mom is the best mom in the world" is an opinion that cannot be fact-checked.

Recognize the power of confirmation bias. This is the human tendency to seek

---

out information that supports personal opinion. Contradictory information tends to be dismissed as false without investigation. Fact-checking requires an openness to exploring new evidence.

Look for statistical fallacies. These are errors in data analysis used to support a viewpoint.

– generalization, or assuming that findings of a small or non-representative sample applies to a large population. *A neighborhood poll showed that 75% favor limits on the number of dogs owned. A state law on limiting dog ownership is likely to pass.*

– post hoc ergo propter hoc, or assuming causation if one event occurs before another. This fallacy is similar to correlation-equals-causation in which co-occurring events are assumed to be causally related. *My dad lost weight when we bought an air fryer. Air fryers promote weight loss.*

– proof by lack of evidence. *Bigfoot must be real because I haven't seen any evidence that he doesn't exist.*

Research the sources and not just the information. Some information is available in public records that can be considered unbiased and trustworthy. Other information is from periodicals, websites, or groups that may have a bias. Find out whether the source has endorsed a political party, has supported a certain agenda, or receives a large amount of advertising revenue from a particular company. If it has, investigate the political party, agenda, or company as well.

Find the original source of the information you are fact-checking. Look up the study, interview, or media to verify its accuracy. Get the date and location of original sources and make sure they aren't being presented in a misleading way. For example, a video clip of a politician saying, "My goal isn't to run for president" has a different meaning when separated from the next sentence: "My goal is to *be* the president."

Consider both sides of a debate. If the facts you're checking are part of a controversial issue, determine the primary arguments used by each side. For example, search "why achievement testing should be mandatory" and "why achievement testing should be banned." Try using more than one search engine to see if you get different results.

Ignore ad hominem attacks (criticisms of the person or group that aren't relevant to the issue) when you are evaluating the claims. *The mayor says that most people in the city want pet ownership limited to two dogs. But you should know that he isn't a dog lover; he only has a cat.*

> **Be willing to reevaluate.** The data may not support a position now, but as more study is done, you may have to change your assessment of claims.

Luke whistled. "One thing I know for sure. I don't want to be a fact checker. Too much work!"

Ellen frowned. "You're not going to like my idea then," she said.

Luke sighed. "Let me guesss. We're sending out a mission."

"Yes. But this is a very important mission. We are going to volunteer to be fact-checkers for social media posts! If we do it well, we can reduce conflict, starting with Mother and Father."

The two boys agreed and got to work on a mission called Fact-Checking.

What does *unwitting* mean?

What is an ad hominem attack?

Who is the most likely backer of the Citizen Fact-Checkers?

Asteroid on Track to Destroy Planet English

Chapter 3

"Have you seen this?" Ellen received this message from her friend that included a link to a news article. "Asteroid on Track to Destroy Planet English" was the headline. Ellen gasped and clicked through to skim the first paragraph.

"The asteroid is headed to planet English in two months, scientists say," she read. "Oh no," she whispered aloud.

"Is there anything your father can do?" her friend messaged.

Ellen didn't immediately answer, but her thought was clear: no. There was nothing her father could do about a giant asteroid that would **obliterate** everything in its path, including the people on her home planet. She knew her father. He overreacted to grammar issues and the

★ ★ ★ ★ ★ ★ ★ ★ ★

obliterate – *destroy*

★ ★ ★ ★ ★ ★ ★ ★ ★

19

Gremlin's attempts to malign him. But he didn't seem worried about true catastrophes like this one.

Ellen knew that if this crisis could be averted, it would be up to her to take action. "Don't worry," she messaged back. "We have a plan." She chewed her fingernail anxiously. "I just don't know what it is yet," she said aloud.

Ellen thought about talking to Kirk, but he wasn't likely to take the threat seriously, either. She didn't want to use Screen to search for a solution. The results would likely be restricted to avoid panicking the citizens. She wanted the truth, no matter how unnerving it was. It was the only way to avoid the impending disaster.

She went to the computer lab and began searching for solutions to the asteroid impact. She skimmed the results until she found an article that looked promising.

The author said that the only real solution was to abandon planet English and relocate to other planets in the galaxy. Planet Vocabulary was a particulary good choice, the author wrote, because the number of occupants had been declining in recent years. While it is sad to have to leave our home, the article continued, it was time for the king of Grammar Galaxy to accept the science and save his people by relocating them now.

"Of course!" Ellen said aloud. "Father would never want to evacuate planet English, but we have to if we're going to survive." She began thinking about how difficult it was to change her father's mind about things and realized that she couldn't wait for that. She would have to **devise** another reason that people needed to leave the planet.

★ ★ ★ ★ ★ ★ ★ ★ ★ ★

devise – *create*

★ ★ ★ ★ ★ ★ ★ ★ ★ ★

At dinner that evening, Ellen started to make a case for leaving the planet. "Father, you know how we go to the other planets in the galaxy whenever there's a problem?"

"Yes," the king said between bites of his meal.

"Well, why aren't we spending time on these planets to prevent crises in the first place?" she asked.

The king stopped eating and stared at her. "Preventive visits then?" he asked.

"Yes, but it shouldn't just be a quick visit. I think we need to really live with the words and letters in the galaxy in order to protect them."

"How long are you thinking?" he asked her.

"Oh, I don't know. It would be an extended visit, though, so we would need to take most of our belongings," she explained tentatively.

"We would need multiple shuttles to take most of our belongings," the king joked.

"I know you're kidding, but it would be a lot of shuttle trips to take everyone's belongings," Ellen said.

"Multiple shuttle trips to take our family's things?" The king was taken aback.

"Oh, no. I'm talking about all the guardians' belongings and their families' things," Ellen said **placidly**.

★ ★ ★ ★ ★ ★ ★ ★ ★ ★

placidly – *calmly*

★ ★ ★ ★ ★ ★ ★ ★ ★ ★

"You want everyone to visit the other planets in the galaxy for an extended period. So we're going to leave planet English unattended?" The king chuckled, but Ellen did not.

"Ellen, are you feeling all right?" The queen stood up to feel her forehead.

"Yes, I'm fine," Ellen said steadily. "I feel really strongly about this. It's the only way."

"The only way for what?" Luke asked.

"The only way to…to prevent crises," Ellen said haltingly.

"I approve of your preemptive approach, Ellen. I really do. But we can't relocate the entire planet, even for a short visit," the king said carefully.

Ellen's eyes welled with tears. "But you have to do it! Our future depends on it." Ellen stood up and asked to be excused, saying she had no appetite.

"Weird," Luke said when she was gone.

The queen gave him a look to silence him, but she was thinking the same thing.

Later that evening, the queen mentioned Ellen's odd suggestion while they were watching the news. The king didn't have a chance to respond before the news anchor said, "Our top story tonight is the asteroid that is on its way to planet English. Scientists have been tracking it, and…"

The king turned to his wife. "That's it."

"What is?" the queen asked.

"The asteroid is what has Ellen wanting to evacuate the planet,"

"Oh my. What are you going to do?"

"I'm going to evacuate the planet." When the queen gasped, he said he was kidding.

"Not funny. What are you really going to do?" she asked.

"I'm going to review science reading with the kids. They need to understand that we can't let the media interpret science for us."

The next morning, the king read the article on science reading to his children.

Science Reading

Comprehension of science texts improves when students:

Learn the vocabulary. Look up the definition of new terms in the article. Then use a known synonym, illustrate the word, or dramatize the new word to aid memory.

Make connections to the text. Before reading a science article, view examples of the concept. Go on a field trip. Discuss news stories or personal experiences related to the science.

Review text visuals. Look at pictures, charts, and graphs before reading and predict what the article's main point is before reading.

Take notes. Review small portions of the text at a time. Note the most important information in these portions and summarize it in your own words.

Use the information in a hands-on way. Complete an experiment, build a model, or sketch the process that you've learned about.

When the king finished reading, he said, "Let's take the asteroid that the media is telling us is on target to destroy us as an example."

Ellen gasped. *He knew about the asteroid!*

"I found an article in a science journal on the subject, the king continued. "Screen, would you pull it up, please?"

The king read a sentence aloud. "In the year 3030, asteroid 4680 will come within 31,000 kilometers of planet English."

"It's not coming until 3030? Why are they talking about it now?" Ellen asked with annoyance.

"Yeah, and it's not even going to hit us," Luke interjected.

"Right. The media usually makes science articles sound more interesting and impactful (sorry for the pun) than they are. Scary content sells more than dry, scientific content does."

"Uh-oh," Ellen said, blanching. "I may have told my friends that we had to relocate to avoid being destroyed by the asteroid."

"You're not the first to be deceived by these kinds of stories, Ellen. That's why I want you to send a mission on science reading. I do think your idea of doing preventive visits to the planets in our galaxy was a good one, however." The king smiled and side hugged his daughter.

The four of them began work on a science-reading mission right away.

What does *obliterate* mean?

What are some hands-on activities for remembering science information?

Why didn't Ellen tell her father the real reason for her plan?

Chapter 4

The king was eager to check the paper in the morning. The Librarians' Choice for Children book list was due. There it was, beginning on the front page. Students looked forward to the book list as did teachers and librarians. The titles chosen would be the most read in the galaxy for the upcoming year. Many of them would win at the Annual Book Awards because of the publicity.

As the king scanned the list, he admitted to himself that he wasn't familiar with them. He liked to read popular children's books, but as his kids had gotten older and were reading independently, it was harder to make time for them. He hoped his wife had read them and could **attest** to their quality.

★ ★ ★ ★ ★ ★ ★ ★ ★ ★

attest – *confirm*

★ ★ ★ ★ ★ ★ ★ ★ ★ ★

"Dear, the Librarians' Choice for Children list is out. Have you read these titles?" he asked. He then began reading them to his wife.

"No. Hm. Sounds familiar, but no. I think my friend read that one, but I haven't," the queen said after each title was read. "It's sad that I haven't read these. I've been so busy," the queen said.

"You should never be too busy to read," the king said, regretting his words immediately.

The queen's eyes blazed. "Have *you* read these books?" she asked as a challenge.

"No," the king said apologetically.

"You're not saying you've been too busy," the queen asked sarcastically.

"I was wrong to say that. The truth is I feel guilty that I haven't been reading these books," the king said, shoulders sagging.

"I appreciate your honesty," the queen said, feeling bad about her sarcasm. "We can commit to reading these going forward, right?" she said to cheer him.

"Right. It will be wonderful discussing them with you," the king said. He smiled and hugged his wife.

Later the king received a video call from the Prime Minister. "Your Highness, good to see you," he said. "I expect you have seen the Librarians' Choice list. I wanted to get your thoughts."

"My thoughts? Oh, yes. I did review the list," the king stammered.

"And? You approve?" the Prime Minister asked.

"Uh, yes. I mean, our librarians know quality literature when they read it."

"Right. But you approve of the collection of titles?" the Prime Minister pressed him.

The king was getting irritated. "Yes, why wouldn't I?" he said.

"Well," the Prime Minister started. "Never mind. If you're okay with the list, so am I," he said, shrugging.

"Yes, yes. Let's focus on more **pressing** issues, shall we?" the king said.

★ ★ ★ ★ ★ ★ ★ ★ ★ ★

pressing – *urgent*

bluff – *deceive*

★ ★ ★ ★ ★ ★ ★ ★ ★ ★

The Prime Minister changed the subject to one he knew would cheer the king: The pages-read statistic in the galaxy was climbing.

That afternoon the king admitted to the queen that he'd had to **bluff** his way through the chat with the Prime Minister. The queen was concerned about the Prime Minister's questions. "I think we need to fast-track our plan to read these books. We can have the kids help us."

The king agreed with the plan, and they pitched it to the children as a fun family activity. "We will read the books on the list. Then we'll come together to have a discussion of the book list as a whole," the king said enthusiastically.

Luke shrugged but agreed.

A couple of weeks later the family met in the castle library to discuss the books they'd read.

"I enjoyed the books I read a lot. They were short—." Ellen started but was interrupted by Luke.

"I always enjoy short books," he joked.

25

"Luke, that was rude," Ellen said, frowning. "As I was saying, they were short picture books with beautiful illustrations. One book was about a prince. The other was about a princess."

"Did the prince get killed by a dragon who became king? Because that's what happened in my book," Luke interjected.

"What? No!" Ellen exclaimed. "Let me finish. In my book, the prince decided to be a farmer. He lived happily ever after."

"What about the princess book?" the queen asked.

"She kills her sister so she can be queen," Ellen stated matter-of-factly.

The queen gasped. "In a picture book?"

"It didn't have any blood," Ellen assured her.

"The book I read was about a prince, too," Kirk said. "He killed the king and gave the castle and all the property to the people," he explained.

"I think I've heard enough," the king said with an edge to his voice.

"But I haven't said what my book was about," the queen complained.

"I already know," the king said. When the queen questioned him, he explained. "All of the books chosen for the Librarians' Choice for Children award seem to be the same. The Gremlin must have had a librarian on the committee." When his family didn't nod to express their understanding, he removed *The Guide to Grammar Galaxy* from its shelf and read them the article on theme.

Theme

Theme is the meaning or message of a book, poem, or movie.

Some common themes are love conquers all; crime doesn't pay; we are our own worst enemy; we can achieve the impossible with enough effort; money is the root of all evil, and technology will destroy humanity.

Themes are the author's opinion on common subjects such as love, death, human nature, overcoming struggles, growing up, family, good vs. evil, the meaning of life, money, friendship, technology, people vs. nature, people vs. society, and war. There may be multiple themes, but there is usually a primary theme.

To discover the theme of a work, state the plot in one sentence. The plot is not the same as the theme but will give you clues about it. Remember that plot is a problem and a solution. The problem in Cinderella was her mistreatment by her

---

stepfamily. The solution was the prince meeting and choosing her for his bride at the royal ball. So, Cinderella's plot is: A mistreated stepdaughter attends the royal ball and is chosen by the prince as his bride over her mean stepsisters.

Next, note the subject. In addition to the plot, what is the book about? Cinderella is a fairy tale and like many fairy tales is about good vs. evil. A less important subject of Cinderella is love. Many literary works cover more than one subject.

Finally, determine the author's attitude toward the problem and solution. What is the author trying to say? These answers will make the theme clearer. In Cinderella, the author seems to enjoy Cinderella's happiness at the stepfamily's expense. The author seems to be saying that good will eventually win over evil.

If you are correct about the theme, you should be able to find examples to support it. Examples will include characters' actions and quotes. In many versions of Cinderella, the girl is described as "good" and "kind." Her stepsisters are described as "ugly" and "mean." The stepfamily is shocked by the prince's choice of Cinderella as his bride. In some versions, they beg Cinderella for forgiveness. They are either sent away or forgiven, depending on the author's view of what good winning over evil looks like.

"All of the books chosen for the list have the same theme. That's why the Prime Minister wanted to know my reaction," the king said.

"Can't you have the list changed?" Ellen asked.

"I'm afraid not. But what I can do is have the guardians review theme, so they will know that these books were chosen for a reason."

"You want us to send out a theme mission?" Kirk asked.

"Yes, right away," the king said.

What does *pressing* mean in the story?

Themes are the author's _____ on common subjects.

What is the theme for the books on the Librarians' Choice for Children book list?

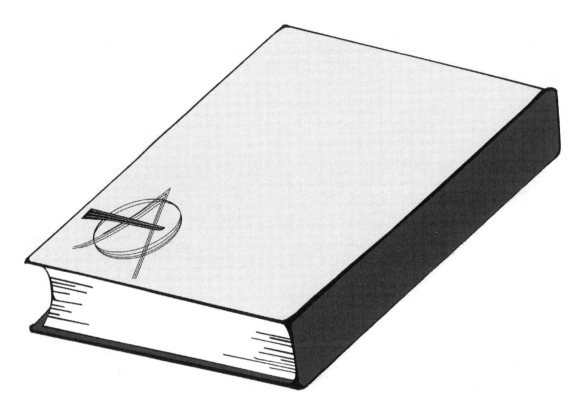

Chapter 5

The king noticed Ellen reading alone in the sunroom. "You seem to be **relishing** your book," he said.

★ ★ ★ ★ ★ ★ ★ ★ ★ ★

relishing – *enjoying*

★ ★ ★ ★ ★ ★ ★ ★ ★ ★

Ellen was startled to hear his voice. "Oh, I didn't hear you come in." She seemed disoriented as she looked around her.

"It must be a really good book," the king said, chuckling. When Ellen didn't laugh, he frowned. "Are you okay?"

"Yes, yes," Ellen replied breathlessly. "It's just this book. It's a little creepy."

"I'm surprised that you're reading a scary book. I didn't think you liked them."

"I know. I don't. My friend recommended it," she said to explain.

"I see," the king said. He smiled and told her she didn't have to keep reading it.

"I know," Ellen said, smiling in return. "It's good, though."

28

"Could I see it?" the king asked, holding his hand out. The title of the book was *Dark Winter.* A gray castle was nearly **obscured** by a thick forest of trees in silhouette on the cover. He flipped the book to read the description on the back.

★ ★ ★ ★ ★ ★ ★ ★ ★ ★
obscured – *hidden*
despotic – *tyrannical*
★ ★ ★ ★ ★ ★ ★ ★ ★ ★

The king and his castle were relics of a gloomy past. The few survivors who had lived under his **despotic** rule assumed the old monarch was dead. But they were wrong.

The castle, though dark and in disrepair, was teeming with life. Ravens perched in the beams of the great hall and squawked with confidence each evening. Rats scurried through the kitchen, arranging trinkets and food scraps left behind by curious hikers. Foxes walked the perimeter of the castle, smiling in anticipation of the dark winter to come.

"I see it's another book with an anti-monarchy theme," he said, frowning. Ellen shrugged.

The king scanned to the bottom of the back cover to see who had published it. "Revolution Publishers," he said aloud. "And what a logo they have," he said disapprovingly.

"What do you mean?" Ellen asked.

The king showed her the red A in a circle.

"Why is that bad?" she asked.

"It's a symbol for anarchy," the king explained. "That's what the Gremlin wants, believe me."

"Or it could be the first initial of the owner of the publisher," Ellen suggested.

The king shook his head. "Not with the other symbolism in the book."

"What other symbolism?" she asked.

The king sighed. "I want to answer the question when your brothers can hear," he said soberly.

He had the boys join them in the sunroom and bring him *The Guide to Grammar Galaxy* from the castle library.

"We have reviewed theme with the guardians," he began when they arrived, "so they know the Gremlin is trying to turn public opinion against us with books. But that's not his only tactic. I think he is using symbolism as well. I want to review the information on symbolism from the guidebook with you." The king read the article aloud.

Symbolism
A symbol is a setting, character, event, or object in a story that has a deeper meaning. Symbols are literal (observable) and figurative (metaphorical).   The ring in *The Lord of the Rings* symbolizes power and evil.   The lion in *The Lion, The Witch, and the Wardrobe* symbolizes power and authority.   The garden in *The Secret Garden* symbolizes a safe place.   An entire plot can be symbolic. Symbolic plots are called allegories. The plot of the movie *Wall-E* symbolizes saving the earth. The book *The Sneetches* by Dr. Seuss symbolizes racism.   Authors can create new symbolism in their work or rely on accepted meanings. Some commonly understood symbols are listed in the following chart.   Note that too many symbols in a literary work can make it silly.

Symbolism Chart	
SETTINGS **Forest:** often evil, the unknown **Desert:** loneliness **Garden:** paradise or safe place **Spring:** fresh start **Winter:** death **Dawn, light, candle:** hope **Darkness, night:** danger **Fog:** confusion **Thunder, fire:** punishment	**Rainbow:** good fortune **Rain:** sadness **Storms:** strong emotions **Lightning:** power **Apple:** temptation **Weeds:** evil **Rose:** romance **Water:** purity **Evergreen tree:** eternal life

Symbolism Chart	
COLORS **Black:** death, evil **White:** good **Red:** emotion **Green:** life	**Blue:** peace **Yellow:** aging **Gold:** wealth **Purple:** royalty
OBJECTS **Cloak:** trickery **Mask:** demonic **Skull:** death **Crown:** power **Key:** answer **Heart:** love	**Circle:** perfection **Pearl:** purity **Ring:** commitment **Sword:** protection **Axe:** work
ANIMALS **Dove:** peace **Eagle:** freedom **Lion, bear:** power **Dog:** loyalty **Butterfly:** change	**Fox, cat:** clever **Peacock:** pride **Raven:** death **Owl:** wisdom **Lamb:** gentleness

"If the Gremlin is going to use symbolism to attack us, what can we do about it?" Kirk asked.

"Should we ban symbolism?" Luke asked.

The king laughed. "We can't do that any more than we can change the list of books on the Librarians' Choice for Children list. But we can make sure that the guardians understand symbolism in what they read," he said.

"We're sending out a mission on symbolism then?" Ellen asked.

"Yes," the king answered. "Perhaps we can have them read books that have positive symbolism as well as the negative the Gremlin seems so fond of."

What does *obscured* mean?

What are symbolic plots called?

Why did the king think *Dark Winter* was anti-monarchy?

Chapter 6

"Good morning!" the queen said enthusiastically as the children entered the dining room.

"What's good about it?" Luke snarled.

The queen caught the king's eye with a look that asked him to respond.

"What did you mean to say, Luke?" the king asked.

Luke sighed. "I meant to say good morning," he said in a dull voice.

"Good morning," Kirk said, sighing heavily.

The queen looked to Ellen for a response. "What?" she snapped.

"Oh, dear," the queen said, dismayed. "I assume this means you three stayed up too late."

"No," Ellen retorted. "Why do you always assume that?" she asked, almost sneering.

"Yeah, some mornings just aren't good," Luke agreed.

The queen's eyes welled with tears. "Well, forgive me for being cheerful," she said before running to her bedchamber.

"Now you've done it," the king said.

"Now we've done what?" Ellen asked **nonchalantly,** examining her nails.

★ ★ ★ ★ ★ ★ ★ ★ ★ ★

nonchalantly – *indifferently*

★ ★ ★ ★ ★ ★ ★ ★ ★ ★

"You've upset your mother and you know that," the king said, his voice rising. He looked around the table at his children's faces and tried to calm himself. "I want to know. Did you stay up late?"

"No!" Ellen yelled. She cowered when she saw her father's angry reaction. "I mean no," she whispered.

The two boys shook their heads. They hadn't stayed up late either.

"Then where are these attitudes coming from?" he asked.

The children stared at him blankly.

Is this what it's like having teens? the king wondered.

"All right. The three of you have your breakfast. Then you are going to write a letter to your mother apologizing for your insolence," the king said.

"Why do you have to use such big words?" Luke whined.

The king's eyes blazed.

"Okay, okay. We'll do it," Luke said apologetically. He slumped in his chair and picked at the food in front of him.

The king finally excused them to go write apologies. When they had gone, he was determined to find a solution to his children's bad behavior. "Screen," he commanded, "look up how to respond to bad attitudes in teens."

"Your Highness, these are the top-rated tips I found. They don't get good reviews for effectiveness, however. One, have your teen get a job," Screen reported.

"Get a job? They already have jobs," the king said. "What else?"

"Require them to do chores."

"They have to do chores. But they could certainly be doing more. Hm. I could have them clean out the cellar. That would teach them," the king thought, smiling. "Thank you, Screen!" he said before leaving to talk to his wife.

The queen was lying in bed, sniffling.

The king went to her and stroked her hair tenderly. "It's going to be okay," he said. "I have a plan."

"It won't work," the queen said.

The king frowned. "You don't even know what my plan is," he said.

"I don't have to know. I'm a terrible mother and there's no fixing it," the queen said.

"Dear, you are not a terrible mother. The children are just in a teen phase. I'm going to have them clean the cellar. They'll learn that disrespect isn't tolerated in our family. Do you want to tell them what you want done?" the king asked.

"No. It won't matter," the queen said sighing.

The king frowned. "You're always the optimist. I'm the **pessimist**," he said trying to get a reaction.

★ ★ ★ ★ ★ ★ ★ ★ ★ ★

pessimist – *doubter*

★ ★ ★ ★ ★ ★ ★ ★ ★ ★

But the queen continued to cry silently.

"Okay. I'll give you a report on the cellar," the king said, patting her arm. "You rest."

When he had closed his bedchamber door, the king walked quickly to his study. When he arrived, he immediately asked Screen for the tone and mood of the month.

"I don't think that information will do any good," Screen replied. "But the tone is angry and the mood is hopeless."

"Of course it is," the king said with a smile.

The king left to find his children. Each of them was in bed, staring **listlessly** at the ceiling. He had them follow him to the castle library.

★ ★ ★ ★ ★ ★ ★ ★ ★ ★

listlessly – *lethargically*

★ ★ ★ ★ ★ ★ ★ ★ ★ ★

"Which would you rather do, clean the cellar or send out a mission?" he asked them.

Luke groaned. "Neither," he said.

"That's not an option, but both is," the king said sternly.

"Send out a mission," Kirk replied quickly.

The king responded. "Very well. I discovered why you have bad attitudes. Remember when there was a mood and tone of the month? The Gremlin arranged that and, of course, he didn't choose anything positive. He's at it again. I want to review tone and mood with you." He then read aloud from *The Guide to Grammar Galaxy*.

Tone & Mood in Literature

Tone and mood can help the reader understand the theme or main idea of a literary work.

Tone is the author's attitude toward the characters, events, and audience. Tone is determined by the vocabulary used and the syntax or arrangement of words. Tone may be described as serious, lighthearted, sarcastic, depressed, humorous, wary, and more. Edward Lear's "There Was an Old Man Who Supposed" has a mocking, teasing tone.

There was an Old Man who supposed,
That the street door was partially closed;
But some very large rats ate his coats and his hats,
While that futile [pointless] old gentleman dozed.

Mood is the feeling or atmosphere of a piece of literature that is most notable at its beginning. The setting, illustrations, and vocabulary are used to create mood. Mood may be romantic, mournful, cheerful, hopeless, optimistic, playful, etc. The beginning lines of "Drowned at Sea" by Henry Kendall create a dark, depressing mood.

Gloomy cliffs, so worn and wasted with the washing of the waves,
Are ye [you] not like giant tombstones round those lonely ocean graves?

"Do you want us to clean the cellar to teach us about a gloomy mood? Because that would do it," Ellen said.

"No, I wanted you to clean the cellar to teach you about respect," the king retorted a bit too sternly.

"I assume you want us to send this information to the guardians. But how do we change the tone and mood?" Kirk asked.

"Good question. Last time your mother handled the problem with the committee in charge. I can ask her to do that again, but in the meantime, having the guardians read books with a positive tone and mood will help significantly," the king said.

The children nodded and agreed to work together on a mission called Tone & Mood.

What does *listlessly* mean?

Which aspects of literature are used to create mood?

Why didn't the children respond well to their mother's morning greeting?

Chapter 7

The king was in his study, enjoying a quiet morning. Comet was curled up at his feet.

Ellen knocked on his door and handed her diary to him. "Someone rewrote my diary," she said, choking back tears.

"What on English? Who would do that?" he asked, scanning the pages. "Isn't this your handwriting?"

"Yes," she whimpered. "They had to have practiced it to make it so accurate."

"Did they add things to it that aren't true? Some **salacious** event to **debase** the family?" the king asked, his voice rising.

"No, I don't think so. But I haven't read the whole thing," Ellen answered hesitantly.

★ ★ ★ ★ ★ ★ ★ ★ ★ ★

salacious – *scandalous*

debase – *shame*

★ ★ ★ ★ ★ ★ ★ ★ ★ ★

"No?" the king repeated. "I don't understand then. How do you know they rewrote it?" he asked.

"Read it," she said, gesturing to the diary.

"Ellen went shopping with Cher and Zoe and their moms and found the cutest shoes," the king read aloud. "You didn't find cute shoes?" he asked, frowning.

"No!" Ellen replied impatiently.

Before she could explain, the king wondered aloud why anyone would write that his daughter found cute shoes when she hadn't.

"That's not what I mean. Why would I write it that way? 'Ellen went shopping...'" she explained.

The queen interrupted their conversation, entering the study without knocking. "Someone hacked into our computer system and rewrote my mystery novel," the queen said, crying. "It's ruined!" she wailed, covering her face with her hands.

Ellen and the king exchanged looks.

The king put his arm around his wife to comfort her and Comet did his part by licking her leg.

"Dear, I don't think your novel has been hacked," the king said.

"You haven't seen it! It's horrible. It's been rewritten like the narrator is the protagonist. Sometimes I wish I wasn't part of a royal family. We're constantly a target," the queen said, sniffling. Ellen took a turn consoling her.

The king thought better of trying to change his wife's mind and asked Screen for help. "What is happening on planet Composition?" he asked. "I'm interested in Point of View Park in particular."

Before Screen could respond, the queen asked him why he wanted to know about the park. "A vacation isn't going to make me feel better," she said miserably. "But it's nice of you."

Screen interjected. "The current maestro in the park has been put on leave. He has been temporarily replaced with the previous maestro—the one you fired. The restored maestro issued a press release stating that he has the full support of the Equal Rights for Pronouns Association. He said he is committed to allowing all pronouns a chance to be first.

"Oh my word. Not him again," the king groaned. He asked Ellen to find the boys and return to his study with *The Guide to Grammar Galaxy*.

When they arrived, he explained the situation to Kirk and Luke.

"I thought something was **peculiar**," Luke said. "My graphic novel uses the pronoun *you*."

★ ★ ★ ★ ★ ★ ★ ★ ★ ★

peculiar – *strange*

★ ★ ★ ★ ★ ★ ★ ★ ★ ★

"And my computer guidebook is using *he* and *she* instead of *you*," Kirk added.

"I'm not surprised. But before we continue our discussion, I want to review point of view from the guidebook with you," the king said.

Point of View

Point of view refers to who is telling the story. There are three points of view in literature: first person, second person, and third person.

First-person point of view gives just one character's take on events, usually the protagonist's (main character's). First person uses the pronouns *I*, *me*, and *mine*. First-person point of view is used in diaries and autobiographies but is also used in some novels.

Second-person point of view is the least common. It discusses the reader and uses the pronouns *you* and *your*. Second person is often used in how-to books. Instructions are often written in second person with the *you* pronoun being understood and not written (i.e., *Preheat the oven* instead of *You preheat the oven*).

Third-person point of view describes the action from all the characters' standpoints. But usually, it gives only one main character's thoughts. Third person uses the pronouns *he*, *she*, and *it*. Third person is a common point of view for fiction.

"What a mess the maestro has made," the queen said. "What are you going to do about it?" she asked her husband. "Fire him again?"

"No. I have a better idea. I'm going to send the guardians to the park to help the maestro out," he said, grinning.

The queen smiled in return. "You're thinking he'll quit?"

"Exactly," the king answered. "The bonus is that the guardians will get plenty of practice with point of view."

The three English children worked together to create a point-of-view mission and made plans to visit the park with their friends.

39

What does *debase* mean?

Which point of view is the least common?

Why were the diary and the mystery novel different?

Chapter 8

"What are you three up to today?" the king asked the children at breakfast.

"I'm going to organize my room," Ellen said. "Mother and I have an idea for how to rearrange the furniture when I'm finished."

"I'm going to start building a new model spacecraft," Kirk answered before taking a bite of scone.

"I'm playing spaceball with friends," Luke said cheerfully.

"Luke, don't you have a paper due for History Month?" his mother asked.

"Yes, but I'll have plenty of time to work on it later," he replied nonchalantly.

Menacing music began playing *duhn, duhn, duhn.*

"Very funny, Kirk," Luke chided him.

"What did I do?" Kirk asked innocently.

★ ★ ★ ★ ★ ★ ★ ★ ★ ★

menacing – *ominous*

pensively – *musingly*

brooded – *ruminated*

★ ★ ★ ★ ★ ★ ★ ★ ★ ★

"You played that music to say I wasn't going to get my paper done," Luke said.

Before Kirk could reply, the queen spoke. "My sister accused me of trying to make her look bad. I corrected her grammar privately because I didn't want her to embarrass herself."

"Aunt Iseen is mad at you?" Ellen asked.

"I don't think so. That was a long time ago," the queen answered **pensively**.

"Oh. I thought this had just happened," Ellen said, relieved for her mother.

"Leo accused Luke of breaking his robot. I felt caught in the middle," Kirk **brooded**.

"Again?" the queen asked, her brows raised.

"Don't you remember, Mother? You helped us work out the conflict," Kirk said matter-of-factly.

"Yes, I remember, but I thought it had happened again," she said, a little annoyed that Kirk had brought it up.

"Did you say it was History Month, Luke?" the king asked.

The music played *duhn, duhn, duhn* again and Ellen screamed.

"It's creepy music, but it's not scream-worthy," Luke joked.

"No, no, didn't you see that?" Ellen asked, frantically pointing at the wall behind the dining room table.

"See what?" Luke asked.

"That ghost," she said, trembling and hugging her knees to her chest.

"Ghost?" Luke said, laughing. "There is no such thing."

"I know what I saw, Luke," Ellen said, her anger overtaking her fear.

"I was in the hall when I looked up and there was great-grandmama rocking in her chair and laughing at the top of the stairs," the king said quietly.

The rest of the family stared in astonishment at him.

"You saw your great-grandmama's ghost and you didn't tell me?" the queen asked.

"I was three," the king said dreamily.

The queen frowned. "First, we don't have clear memories until at least four. And second, why are you talking about this like it just happened?" she asked.

The king shook his head as if to clear his thinking. "What is happening?" he asked himself aloud. "Luke, you said it's History Month?" he asked again.

Luke nodded.

"The last time it was History Month, we had a problem with flashback. History paragraphs were being added to compositions where they didn't belong. We would share memories without warning, just as we're doing now," the king said.

"Is History Month bringing up ghosts of the past, too? That's the creepiest thing the Gremlin's done," Ellen said, shivering.

"I don't think so, Ellen. Was what you saw a ghost or more of a shadow?" the king asked.

"I guess more of a shadow?" Ellen said uncertainly.

"We were watching a movie. The music played *duhn, duhn, duhn*. I thought Father had upgraded our audio system," Kirk said.

42

"Kirk is having a flashback, but he's right. That's when we discovered that the Foreshadow was on our planet," the king said.

"Not again!" the queen wailed.

"Dear, don't worry. We're going to have the guardians get to work on this crisis. First, we need to review foreshadowing and flashback in the guidebook."

The children followed their father to the castle library and he read two articles to them.

Foreshadowing

Foreshadowing is a literary technique in which clues about future events are given at the beginning of a story. Foreshadowing builds suspense and interest in the plot. It keeps readers reading and viewers watching. Some movie genres use music to draw attention to foreshadowing.

An example of foreshadowing in the Disney film *Bambi* is Bambi's mother warning him of the danger of Man with a gun. This is a clue to his mother being killed by a hunter later in the film.

Flashback

A flashback in a book or movie is an interruption of the present time with a scene from the past. Flashbacks can help explain events and characters' behavior.

Flashbacks in literature should not be overused. They do provide information. But they stop the action that keeps readers and viewers engaged. Use flashbacks sparingly, keep them short, and don't use them near the beginning of a story.

Flashbacks may be identified using the following as clues: a line break in the text, references to the past (e.g., an hour earlier), or use of the past perfect tense (e.g., She had struggled with spelling.)

Clues that the book has returned to the present include references to circumstances before the flashback (e.g., The pain in her leg disturbed her thoughts.) or use of simple past tense (e.g., She ate her eggs and asked for help adjusting her pillow.).

"Flashbacks are definitely being overused," Ellen said, frowning.

"And Foreshadow needs to go back to planet Composition so the girls don't freak out," Luke snickered.

"Believe me, you would have freaked out if you'd seen him, too," Ellen argued.

"Okay. Let's stop arguing and get to work," the king said. "I know you have other things you want to do today."

The children agreed and created a mission on foreshadowing and flashbook, hoping the guardians would quickly get the galaxy back to normal.

What does *menacing* mean?

Why do authors use flashback?

Why did the music play when the king asked about History Month?

Chapter 9

The king found Ellen in the sunroom, watching a movie on her tablet. "What are you watching?" he asked.

"It's an old movie Mother said I could watch," she said. "It's pretty good," she said, smiling.

"If Mother said it was good, I'm sure it is," he joked. "Would you like to go to the library's main branch with us today?" he asked.

"Sure!" Ellen said.

The king was glad she still enjoyed going to the library with him, though she was a teen.

An hour later, the king and his three children walked to the library together. As they walked, he told them that he'd been enjoying monarch biographies lately and planned to check out more.

Luke said that he planned to get the next two books in a science-fiction series he was reading. Kirk planned to check out some classics that had been made into graphic novels. And Ellen said she just wanted to browse. She wasn't sure what she was looking for.

The group split up when they arrived at the library, planning to meet at the circulation desk in an hour. The king wanted to have time to read periodicals as well as find new books.

An hour later, Kirk and Luke met the king, holding a short stack of books each. Ellen had a stack of movies.

"Movies?" the king asked, frowning at Ellen. "Where are your books?"

"That old movie Mother recommended has me interested in watching these," Ellen said defensively. "I always get books. I want to get movies this time," she said, pleading.

"I understand you want to watch some movies, but they don't replace books, Ellen. We'll wait a few minutes for you to pick out some books to read."

No one was happy about the **prospect** of waiting on Ellen. Ellen sighed and rolled her eyes and stomped off to find some books to check out.

★ ★ ★ ★ ★ ★ ★ ★ ★ ★

prospect – *possibility*

intervened – *interfered*

★ ★ ★ ★ ★ ★ ★ ★ ★ ★

The king would have to address her disrespectful attitude when they got home, he realized. *It's not asking too much for her to keep reading,* he thought. *Maybe her mother is the problem. She's being soft on her, giving her movies to watch instead.* The king nodded, confident that he was right. He would talk to his wife right away.

Ellen returned to the circulation desk with two books—*Inkheart* and *Bridge to Terabithia*. "Here," she said. "I have books to check out." She stopped short of making an insolent remark when she saw her father's stern look.

When the group arrived home, the king wasted no time talking to the queen about Ellen's behavior. "She told me you recommended a movie for her to watch. She loved it! So, guess how many books she checked out before I **intervened**?" he asked angrily. Without waiting for a response, he yelled, "None! That's how many. She had a stack of movies to check out instead. I had to send her back to get books and then she gave me attitude," he huffed.

The queen's face reddened as she worked to contain her own anger. "Allow me to clarify," she began slowly. "Ellen loved the movie I recommended, correct?"

"Yes," the king answered reluctantly.

"She wanted to check out more movies from the library, right?"

"Yes."

"You were upset that she hadn't checked out any books. You sent her to get some and she did, but she was disrespectful."

"That's exactly right."

"Have you talked to her about the disrespect?"

"No."

"That needs to happen right away," the queen said.

"I agree, but what about the books?" the king asked.

"What *about* the books? You're upset that she wanted to watch more movies?" the queen asked, eyebrows raised.

"You're not?" the king said, increasing his volume. "She is a guardian. It's her duty to read good literature!"

"Dear, do you not remember that at one time in this galaxy, reading fiction was considered a waste of time?" the queen asked.

"That was a long time ago," the king grumbled, pacing around.

"Even so, at the time, people felt very strongly that children shouldn't read novels," the queen said calmly. "Today, many people (including you apparently) believe that movies are a waste of time. But movies are literature. They can be studied just like books, and we can benefit from watching quality films."

"Hmph," the king grunted, annoyed that the queen was right. "So, you're saying that I should let Ellen watch movies?"

"I'm saying that we can use movies to teach literary concepts."

"I suppose you think we should have the children send out a mission on this, too," the king said, smirking.

"I wasn't thinking that, but it's a splendid idea. Why don't you talk with Ellen about her behavior first? Then we can all meet in the castle library to read what the guidebook has to say about movies."

Later, the queen read the article she'd found on the topic aloud to her family.

Movies as Literature

Movies are literature because they include the same literary concepts that are studied in written works.

Silent film actor Charlie Chaplin, who began making films in 1914, said, "Movies are a fad. Audiences really want to see live actors on a stage." Contrary to Chaplin's prediction, the video story form continues to increase in popularity. But the recency and popularity of movies does not make them an inferior literary form. Novels and other fictional works were once considered a waste of students' time. Yet we now know that fictional reading increases vocabulary and empathy.

Study of movies is another worthy academic endeavor. Movies that are book adaptations and those that are stand-alone films are both appropriate for literary analysis.

Study of some movies (as with some books) benefits from background information on the setting or references made. Students are typically directed to look for literary elements while watching the film, such as theme, character development, and climax. Movies offer the additional elements of music, lighting, and **cinematography** to examine.

Answering questions while viewing may interfere with students' comprehension of the film. Reviewing the movie or certain scenes may be required to answer in-depth or detail questions.

Studying films is a particularly effective way of learning about culture and human nature. It provides the opportunity to discuss literature with more people who have viewed a movie but have not read a book.

"So, I'm studying literature when I watch movies?" Ellen asked incredulously.

"Not necessarily," the king responded. "You *can* be studying literature when you watch movies. The quality of the film matters as does your focus when you watch."

"And, of course, we want you to continue reading good books," the queen said, smiling.

"I will!" Ellen promised. "I can't wait to watch the movies I checked out."

★ ★ ★ ★ ★ ★ ★ ★ ★ ★

cinematography – *camerawork*

★ ★ ★ ★ ★ ★ ★ ★ ★ ★

"Before you do, I want the three of you to send out a mission on movies as literature," the king said.

"That's a great idea," Ellen said. "I'll be able to talk about these movies with my friends."

"The other good thing about movies is popcorn! I never eat popcorn when I read," Luke added.

The rest of the family laughed, and the children got to work on the mission.

What does *intervened* mean?

Why are movies literature?

What was the king's attitude toward movies at first?

Unit II: Adventures in Spelling & Vocabulary

Chapter 10

The royal English children were bubbling with excitement about going to Science Camp. They would be staying in Science Galaxy with a large group of guardians for three weeks.

The king had been reluctant to give permission for the children to go. But seeing their excitement, he realized he was glad he had. He knew they would learn a lot. He also liked the king of Science Galaxy, though he didn't understand most of what he said.

He felt better about the children being gone for so long, knowing that they would be in constant contact via communicator. Cook was the most emotional about the trip. She had packed the kids snacks to last them at least a week.

All three of the children hugged and kissed Cook, their parents, and Comet goodbye. They promised to call as soon as they arrived at camp.

The king made sure that his children had plenty of books to take with them. "Remember to read!" he called as their mother guided them into the space copter. The copter would take them to the shuttle terminal where the other guardians were gathering for the trip.

"I'm going to miss them," the king said to Cook.

"Me, too," she sniffled, **ambling** off to the kitchen with Comet at her heels.

★ ★ ★ ★ ★ ★ ★ ★ ★

ambling – *wandering*

capacious – *spacious*

ubiquitous – *abundant*

★ ★ ★ ★ ★ ★ ★ ★ ★

Later that day, Kirk called his mother to say they were all safe and set up in their rooms. "The camp facility is really **capacious**," he said. "And the computers are **ubiquitous**."

Luke and Ellen each took a turn describing the camp. The queen was relieved to hear from them.

The following evening, the king suggested to Cook and the queen that they call the children. They gathered in the media room and asked Screen to place the call to Ellen. When she answered, the king asked her to have the boys join her.

Kirk enthused about the robotics work he had been doing. Ellen talked about the chemistry experiments they had been doing to create various scents. But Luke just hung his head.

"Luke, what's wrong? Don't you feel well? Are you missing home?" the queen asked with a worried frown.

"No, I'm fine," Luke said, sighing.

"What have you been doing?" the king asked to distract him.

"We've been doing dissections," he answered, his upper lip trembling.

"You don't like it? That seems like something you would enjoy," the queen said.

"It's okay," Luke answered evenly.

"He doesn't like the lab reports," Ellen offered.

Luke elbowed her.

"That's what you told me," she protested.

"The lab reports are fine. It's just..." Luke said, trailing off.

"They won't let him dictate them," Ellen said, moving away from Luke's elbow.

"You have to hand-write the notes?" the queen asked.

Luke nodded numbly.

"He doesn't want to misspell words and be embarrassed," Ellen added, still leaning away from Luke.

"That's not—," Luke began angrily, stopping himself. His shoulders slumped. "Yeah, that's true," he admitted. "Why can't I dictate the notes?" he added, shaking his head. "It makes no sense."

"I agree," the king said, irate on his son's behalf. "I'll contact the camp director tomorrow and demand that she allow you to dictate."

"No!" the queen and Luke said together.

"I'll be even more embarrassed then!" Luke cried.

"What he said," the queen agreed. "Dear, there is another way to handle this," she said to the king.

"I don't think bringing him home is the answer," the king retorted.

"I wasn't going to suggest that," the queen said, frowning.

"I was!" Cook interjected. "The poor dear."

The king and queen looked at Cook and smiled.

"I packed you something for just such a situation," the queen said, smiling.

"I did, too!" Cook gushed.

The queen ignored Cook and continued. "I put a phonetic dictionary in your backpack."

"What's a phonetic dictionary?" Luke asked.

"You look up the spelling of words in it based on the sound of the word. Focus on the root word. For example, to look up the spelling of *unbelievable,* you'd look up the word *believe,* ignoring the prefix *un* and the suffix *able*. You'd look up b-e-l-e-v and you'd find the correct spelling of b-e-l-i-e-v-e with several suffixes," the queen explained.

"Do I have to know the exact letters to find the word?" Luke asked.

"No. That's the power of it. There is more than one phonetic spelling for some words," the queen said.

"Wow! That was a great thing to pack, Your Highness," Cook said. "I just packed some of his favorite cookies."

The whole family laughed.

"I'll use those right after the call. Thanks, Cook," Luke said warmly.

"I wonder if some of the other kids at camp could use this dictionary," Kirk said.

"Kirk, that's a splendid idea. Do you have time to send out a quick mission? There are phonetic dictionaries online, but I'll have a shipment of print books sent right away," the king said.

"Yes, we have time. We're on break now, and I can ask Screen to help put a Phonetic Spelling mission together."

The family chatted a little longer and the children promised to send out a mission the next day.

What does *capacious* mean?

What is a phonetic dictionary?

Why wasn't Luke enjoying Science Camp?

Chapter II

The king quickly finished his dinner and suggested they call the children at Science Camp.

"You're really missing them, aren't you?" the queen asked.

"I just want to make sure that they're doing well," the king said, defending himself.

The queen smiled. "I'm sure that's all it is."

"I want to talk to them, too!" Cook called from the kitchen. "I'll be ready as soon as I finish eating—I mean, putting away these leftovers."

The king and queen laughed and assured her they would wait for her.

A few minutes later, the king had Screen call Luke's communicator. "Luke! It's so good to see you. How are things going with the phonetic dictionary?" the king asked.

"And the cookies!" Cook interjected.

Luke laughed. "All good. Thanks, Mother and Cook," he said, rubbing his stomach.

"They're trying to make spelling easier for us now," Kirk said.

"Oh? How is that?" the king asked.

"Only English words will be used."

"Of course, only English words are being used. How will that help?" the king asked, getting irritated.

"They said we won't use any Latin, French, or German spelling."

The king groaned. "I don't know how you're supposed to write lab reports without Latin spelling."

"What do you mean?" Luke asked.

"Remember when we learned about spelling foreign words that are part of the English language? Many science words have Latin spelling. Wait. I'll have *The Guide to Grammar Galaxy* brought in and I'll review it with you." When the book arrived, the king read the article on foreign words.

Foreign Words

Foreign words in the English language are also known as loanwords. The three languages that contribute the most loanwords are Latin, French, and German.

Latin Spelling Tips

The \$\overline{oo}$\ sound is usually spelled with a *u* as in *lucid* and *lunatic* when it follows a \d\, \j\, \l\, \r\, or \s\ sound. After other consonants, it sounds like \yoo\ as in *refugee* or *bugle*.

Some Latin words spell the \s\ sound with sc, including *crescent*, *susceptible*, and *discipline*.

The letter *k* is rarely used in Latin words. Instead, words like *aquatic*, *canine*, and *corporal* are spelled with *c*.

French Spelling Tips

French usually spells \sh\ with *ch* as in *cachet*, *chagrin*, and *quiche*.

French words ending in the \äZH\ sound are spelled *age* as in *collage*, *barrage*,

---

and *garage*.

A \k\ sound at the end of a word is often spelled with *que* as in *physique*, *mystique*, and *boutique*.

German Spelling Tips

The \k\ sound is spelled with *k* at the start of a word or syllable and is spelled with *ck* at the end. For example, *kitsch, kuchen, rucksack*.

The long *i* sound \ī\ is usually spelled *ei* as in *einkorn, eiderdown*, and *Fahrenheit*.

The \sh\ sound is usually spelled *sch* as in *schnauser, anschluss*, and *schottische*.

"They told us not to use foreign spelling. What do we do?" Kirk asked.

"I'll have to talk to the Science king," his father said, sighing.

"You said you wouldn't do that," the queen reminded him.

"I did, didn't I?" the king agreed. "Perhaps the camp director will see that this spelling rule is a terrible idea."

The royal English children agreed that they could let the issue go for now. The family enjoyed a short visit about the food and the other kids they had met at camp.

Two days later, the king called Kirk without the rest of the family. "I want to know how things are going with this spelling nonsense," he said seriously.

"Well, we have another problem. We have some kids attending camp who use British English. The camp has ruled that only British spelling is correct."

"That's **absurd**!" the king exclaimed. "If they're going to keep making **inane** rules like this, I'll just have to bring you three home."

Kirk hung his head and the king noticed. "You don't want to come home," the king said. Kirk shook his head. "All right. I've been too **brash**. What do you think we should do?"

★ ★ ★ ★ ★ ★ ★ ★ ★

absurd – *ridiculous*

inane – *silly*

brash – *hasty*

★ ★ ★ ★ ★ ★ ★ ★ ★

"I think we should send a mission to the guardians. They'll have proof that they are spelling English words with foreign roots. And while we are here, we can use British spelling. We'll remind the guardians of the differences. It's not a big deal," Kirk said shrugging.

"Kirk, you are being more mature about this than I am. I'm proud of you. Would you three send out a mission on foreign words and British spelling?"

Kirk agreed and got to work with Luke and Ellen.

What does *inane* mean?

How do the French usually spell \sh\?

Why was the king so upset about the spelling rules?

Chapter 12

Cook and the queen decided to call Luke at Science Camp when he was alone. The two wanted to make sure he was doing well.

He was excited to get their call. "Do you want me to get Kirk and Ellen?" he asked.

"No, no. We wanted to talk with you. We'll call Ellen and Kirk, too," the queen said, smiling. "It's so good to see you. Here's someone else who misses you," the queen said, holding Comet up to the screen.

"Comet!" Luke exclaimed. "Hey, boy! Aww, I miss him," he said sadly.

"We miss you!" Cook said, her eyes welling with tears. "I have a new batch of treats for you, coming shuttle delivery."

"Shuttle delivery?" the queen gasped and stared at Cook.

"Don't tell the king. I wanted them to be fresh," Cook explained.

The queen laughed. "Luke, how is everything going with spelling now?"

"Okay." He hesitated and the queen noticed.

"What's wrong?"

"Nothing."

"It doesn't sound like nothing."

"Maybe it is, though. We had a guest instructor from Math Galaxy today. She talked about how **imperative** math is in science. Afterward, the director of the camp said we would be graded on our math, too."

★ ★ ★ ★ ★ ★ ★ ★ ★ ★

imperative – *important*

★ ★ ★ ★ ★ ★ ★ ★ ★ ★

"You do well in math, Luke," the queen said, encouraging him.

"I know."

"So you're worrying for nothing, right?" the queen said cheerfully.

Luke waited a moment and then agreed with a smile. "Right. I'm sure looking forward to those treats, Cook!"

"Good! I can't wait to give you a great big hug when you get home," Cook said, air kissing him.

The next day the two women called Ellen. "Did you get the treats I sent?" Cook asked.

"Barely!" Ellen joked. "I had to grab some before Luke ate them all. Thanks so much. And I won't tell Father you had them sent on the shuttle."

"Bless you!" Cook said, and they all laughed.

"How are your grades?" the queen asked.

"Fine," Ellen said flatly.

"What's wrong?" the queen asked.

"Nothing," Ellen said with obvious annoyance.

Cook could tell that the queen was feeling hurt. "We trust you! We just want to help if you need us," Cook told Ellen.

Ellen began crying.

"Oh, Ellen, what's wrong?" the queen asked, her own tears threatening. "Is it the other girls? Do you miss home? Are the boys behaving?"

"No, no, nothing like that," Ellen said, sniffling.

"What is it then?" the queen asked worriedly.

"Is Father around? I'd like to talk to him," Ellen said.

Cook and the queen looked at one another incredulously.

"Sure, sure. I'll get him and give you two some privacy," the queen said.

The queen found the king in his study and briefly explained the situation. The king puffed his chest a little and walked quickly to the media room, pleased that his daughter wanted his help in particular.

"Ellen, so good to see you. How is everything going?" the king asked evenly.

Ellen's throat tightened and she struggled to maintain her **composure** as she talked. "I thought things were going well. I have been getting A's on my science labs until today."

★ ★ ★ ★ ★ ★ ★ ★ ★

composure – *self-control*

★ ★ ★ ★ ★ ★ ★ ★ ★

The king wanted to push her for an explanation, but he remembered his wife saying to reflect back what upset people were saying. Slowly he said, "You were getting A's until today."

"Yes," Ellen nodded. She seemed happy with that response and the king sighed with relief. He would have to thank his wife for that advice. "But today I got my paper back with all kinds of red marks on the numbers. I thought maybe everyone got bad marks. But I asked Luke and his was fine. Maybe I'm just terrible at math and I didn't know!" Ellen wailed.

The king tried to remember what his wife had said to do at times like this. "Don't try to solve the problem right away," she'd said.

"It must be upsetting not to know why you got the bad marks," the king said hesitantly.

"Yes!" Ellen said, wailing loudly.

The king was certain he'd messed up when he remembered the queen saying that good listening **begets** more emotion. "Ellen, could I see your paper? Could you hold it up to the screen?" he asked warmly.

★ ★ ★ ★ ★ ★ ★ ★ ★ ★

begets – *causes*

★ ★ ★ ★ ★ ★ ★ ★ ★ ★

Ellen found the paper and held it up for the king to review. "Mm, I see," the king said.

"I'm terrible at math, right?" Ellen asked, choking back a sob.

"No," the king said, smiling. Your math is correct."

"What? Why is it marked wrong then?"

"You aren't writing with numbers correctly. Will you get the boys on the call? I'm going to get the guidebook," the king said.

Moments later, the king reviewed writing with numbers with his children.

Writing with Numbers

Numbers should sometimes be spelled out and at other times should be left as numerals in writing.

WHEN TO SPELL OUT NUMBERS

- **Numbers one to nine should be spelled out.** The girl grabbed *five* pencils.
- **Numbers at the beginning of a sentence should be spelled out or the sentence rearranged.** *Sixteen* students enrolled in the class. The school enrolled *16* students.
- **When numbers appear next to each other in the text, one number should be spelled out.** He ordered *75 nine*-inch nails.
- **In dialogue or quotes, numbers should generally be spelled out.** "I'm going to need *fifty* cupcakes."

- When spelling out numbers, two-word numbers under 100 should be hyphenated. *"I counted out one hundred twenty-five buttons."*

WHEN TO USE NUMERALS

- Use numerals for dates and numbers larger than nine. By *1865,* more than *600,000* soldiers had died in the Civil War.

- Use numerals for decimals. (Add a zero for decimals less than one.) The chance of being struck by lightning in your lifetime is *0.0003* or 1 in 3000.

- Use numerals to stay consistent in describing something in a sentence, even if it breaks another rule. She counted *5* of *20* pens that worked.

- Use numerals in science writing or directions. Add *4* ounces of vinegar to *2 ½* tablespoons of baking soda.

WHEN TO USE BOTH SPELLING AND NUMERALS

- When writing about millions and billions, mix numerals and words. Over *140 million* books have been published to date.

- When choosing whether to spell a number or use a numeral in writing, use a style guide. Or ask the teacher or publication you're writing for.

"Why am I the only one who didn't remember this?" Ellen complained.

"I'm sure you're not the only one, Ellen," the king said. "In fact—"

"We should send out a mission," Ellen interjected, laughing.

"Right," the king said, smiling.

She and the boys ended the call to work on a writing-with-numbers mission when the queen entered the room.

"Well? What happened? What was wrong?" she asked, wringing her hands.

"It was just daddy-daughter stuff, dear. Don't worry at all," he teased.

"What?" the queen said, shocked that he wasn't telling her the problem.

The king put his arm around her. "Believe it or not, it ended up being a guardian issue."

"Seriously?"

"Seriously. Now does Cook have any of the treats left that she had shuttled to the kids?"

When the queen's eyes widened, he said, "Oh yes. I know about the shuttle." They both laughed.

What does *composure* mean?

What should be done with numbers in dialogue or quotes?

Why was the queen surprised that Ellen wanted to talk to her father?

Chapter 13

Cook had prepared a special meal to welcome the children home from Science Camp. The queen was looking forward to being reunited and having some quiet family time.

The castle was filled with happy children's voices and Comet's barks as the kids came through the door and put their bags down.

"My sweet scientists are home!" Cook declared, warmly hugging each child in turn.

"We missed you so much," the queen said, looking around for the king. "I don't know where your father is, but I'm sure he'll be right out!" she called loudly. She tried to hide her annoyance that he wasn't there to welcome the kids. "He must be on a call. While you're waiting for your father, take your bags to your room and start unpacking."

"We can't," Kirk said. "You can't be so tired that you aren't able to unpack," the queen chided him.

"It's not that," Kirk said.

"No, it's because of bed bugs," Luke said **impishly**.

"Bed bugs? What on English?" the queen exclaimed.

"Bed bugs can hide in your luggage. When you unpack your suitcase in your room, the bugs can get into your bedding. At night they come out and—" Kirk explained.

"And I'm changing the subject," Cook said, shivering. "Just unpack your bags in the laundry room then," Cook said.

"Sorry, Cook. It's science," Luke teased.

When the children left with Cook, the queen went to the king's study. He was having a heated discussion with someone. The queen waited until he ended the call to enter. "The children are home and wondered why you weren't there to greet them," the queen said sanctimoniously.

"I'm sorry, dear, but there is a crisis," the king explained.

"It's always a crisis," the queen complained.

The king reddened. "I suppose you think it's fine that Parliament plans to eliminate the hyphen from the English language." His eyes blazed.

"I can think of more important parts of the language, yes," the queen retorted. The king's mouth was agape. "Don't look at me that way. Your children are more important than hyphens," she lectured.

"I know that!" the king said loudly. "But that doesn't mean that hyphens don't matter at all."

"I assume you'll be able to join us for dinner despite your little punctuation crisis?" the queen asked **haughtily**.

The king remembered his mother saying, "If you don't have anything nice to say, don't say anything at all." He nodded and let his wife leave the room before expressing his frustration.

"The English language will be more confusing, not less without hyphens!" he complained aloud. "Why doesn't Parliament understand that? And why are women so emotional?"

A few hours later, the royal family was seated in the dining room together. The queen asked each of the children to talk about their highs of Science Camp.

"My high was the artificial-intelligence demonstrations we saw," Kirk said.

★ ★ ★ ★ ★ ★ ★ ★ ★

impishly – *mischievously*
haughtily – *arrogantly*

★ ★ ★ ★ ★ ★ ★ ★ ★

"My high was meeting Alyssa. I think we'll be good friends, even though we live far apart," Ellen explained.

"My high was getting treats flown in from Cook," Luke said loudly enough for Cook to hear in the kitchen.

"Your flattery will get you anything you want," Cook called back, laughing.

The king seemed preoccupied. "What about your lows when you were gone?" the king said. "I'll start."

The queen frowned but said nothing.

"Parliament is going to eliminate the hyphen to improve spelling. Can you believe it?" the king groused.

"Oh, that's too bad," Ellen said sympathetically.

"It is bad, isn't it?" he said, looking at his wife victoriously.

"What's bad is that we're talking about grammar the children's first night home," the queen said icily.

The king sighed and **conceded**. "All right. Let's hear more about Science Camp then."

★ ★ ★ ★ ★ ★ ★ ★ ★ ★

conceded – *surrendered*

★ ★ ★ ★ ★ ★ ★ ★ ★ ★

The children talked more about camp during dinner but noticed the tension between their parents.

Ellen asked her brothers to join her in her bedchamber when they were excused from the table. "Mother seems upset," she said.

"So does Father," Luke agreed. "I guess things fall apart when we're gone." He shrugged.

"I don't think that's it," Kirk replied.

"Mother wanted to focus on family our first night home," Ellen said.

"And Father is so worried about the hyphens that he couldn't help but talk about it," Kirk said.

"What do we do? Mother wants to play a board game tonight," Ellen said.

"What if we fixed the hyphen problem so Father can relax?" Luke asked.

"Brilliant! Let's review hyphens in the guidebook," Ellen suggested.

The three of them went to the castle library. Kirk read the article he found on hyphens aloud.

Hyphens

The word *hyphen* is from the Greek word for *together*. Hyphens (-) are used to create some compound words. Note that compound words often begin as separate words. They then become hyphenated and finally become closed compound words with no hyphen. Check a dictionary to determine if a compound word requires a hyphen.

Some examples of hyphenated compound words are check-in, check-up, Commander-in-Chief, President-Elect, mother-in-law, self-esteem, runner-up, singer-songwriter, jack-in-the-box, blue-green, merry-go-round, go-between, pick-me-up, good-for-nothing, two-year-old.

Hyphenate two or more words that describe the following noun. This is called a compound adjective. To determine if it should be hyphenated, ask if each word makes sense describing the noun alone. If not, the words should be hyphenated. Adjective phrases that begin with an -ly adverb and those formed by proper nouns should not be hyphenated.

She was going on a once-in-a-lifetime trip. – *Correct*
The trip was out-of-this-world – *Incorrect, adjectives follow the noun*
That really-moldy doll should be thrown out. – *Incorrect*
The Red-Star guardian got to work. *Incorrect*
Her easy-come-easy-go approach to life causes problems. – Correct
His my way or the highway attitude causes problems. – *Incorrect; it isn't my attitude or highway attitude, so the words my-way-or-the-highway should be hyphenated.*

Hyphens are also used to continue words that are split at the end of a line. The hyphen must appear between syllables. Check a dictionary if you aren't sure where to hyphenate a word.

Her favorite vocabulary word is *sen-*
sational. – *Correct*
His friend's family is thinking about homeschooling. – *Incorrect*

"I think we still need hyphens," Ellen said. "I see why Father is upset."

"What if we send out a mission on hyphens and ask the guardians to write Parliament about the need for them?" Kirk suggested.

"We just got home!" Luke complained.

"I know, but it won't take long to create the mission. The guardians can work on it during the week, but Father will be so relieved," Kirk said.

"Mother, too. She'll be glad we can enjoy playing a game without distractions," Ellen added.

The three children created a mission called Hyphens and went to give their parents the good news.

What does *impishly* mean?

How are hyphens used?

Why were the king and queen in conflict?

Chapter 14

"I'm so nervous!" the queen told Cook after learning she would be emceeing a charity auction.

"I don't know why! You're an excellent speaker," Cook said.

"You're so kind, Cook. But I've never been an emcee before."

"There always has to be a first time," Cook said **sagely**.

★ ★ ★ ★ ★ ★ ★ ★ ★ ★

sagely – *wisely*

★ ★ ★ ★ ★ ★ ★ ★ ★ ★

"That's true! I guess I want to be good at it my first try, which isn't very realistic." The queen smiled gratefully at her friend. "I have something else I wanted to talk with you about. Would you be willing to donate your services for the auction. Don't worry! I would pay you, but we could put one of your dinners up for bidding. In fact, the whole staff could go to the winner's house, and I'll cook that night," the queen explained.

"You would be cooking here?" Cook asked in disbelief.

"That's your question?" The queen pretended to punch Cook's arm playfully. "I can cook for one night."

"I'll just make double of whatever I'm serving," Cook offered, smiling.

"So you'll do it?" the queen asked. She clapped as Cook laughed.

"It would be an honor," Cook said, her eyes glistening. "I'm happy you think so highly of my cooking."

Several weeks later, the queen was getting ready to leave for the auction. The king was attending with her and peppered her with questions. "Do you know what items have been donated? Do you have some jokes ready? Do you know who's coming for sure?"

"You act like you're the one doing the emceeing," the queen teased.

"Did you want me to? I'm not prepared, but I can step in if you need me," the king said earnestly.

"No! Of course not. I'm ready. Don't make me nervous with these **histrionics**," the queen said tersely.

"Sorry. I get nervous when I emcee. I'm assuming you feel the same way," the king said apologetically.

★ ★ ★ ★ ★ ★ ★ ★ ★ ★

histrionics – *dramatics*
introspective – *self-examining*

★ ★ ★ ★ ★ ★ ★ ★ ★ ★

"Wow! You are really becoming **introspective**," the queen said. "Thanks for saying that," she said, hugging his arm. "It's going to be fine! You'll see."

The energy of the auction attendees encouraged the queen. She was feeling more excited and less nervous as she walked to the podium.

"Welcome! Thank you for coming to support literacy in our galaxy. Although raising funds for charity is our goal tonight, we also want you to be happy with your purchases," the queen began.

"Last year, a man bid on a parrot. It was such an unusual item and he really wanted it. But he kept being outbid. Refusing to lose, he kept raising his bid until finally, after committing an exorbitant amount, he'd won. He was ecstatic! But then he started to worry.

"He shared his concern with the auctioneer. 'I sure hope this parrot can talk,' he said. 'I spent a fortune on it and would hate to learn that it can't.'

"'Oh, don't worry,' the auctioneer said. 'He can talk. Who do you think kept bidding against you?'"

The attendees roared with laughter and the king was so proud of his wife.

She was beaming as she continued. "So, I want to ensure you that bidding on any of these items promotes reading."

"*Ensure* you?" the king mumbled to himself. Maybe he'd heard it wrong.

"You can lay down tonight, knowing that you also got a good deal on something you'll enjoy," she said.

"*Lay* down? Did she say *lay* down?" he whispered to himself. "This isn't good. Is she nervous?"

"Just a note that we do have less items to bid on this year. So bid right away to be sure you go home with a prize."

"*Less* items? Now I know there's a problem," the king said to himself. He removed his communicator and messaged Kirk. He explained that his mother was using the wrong words and asked him to get the status on planet Vocabulary right away.

Kirk agreed. He knew how important this auction was to his mother. He notified Luke and Ellen of the issue. They met in the castle library and asked Screen for an update.

"Yes, Your Highness," Screen responded. "The hot topic on the planet Vocabulary is uniforms."

"Uniforms?" Ellen said, wrinkling her nose. "Why do words need uniforms?"

"The sponsor of the program says that uniforms decrease competition between words," Screen said.

"Shouldn't that be *among* words?" Kirk asked.

"That's what I said," Screen answered.

Kirk's eyes widened. "Okay, thank you, Screen," he said to dismiss him.

"The uniforms they picked out are probably not flattering for all words," Ellen said, shaking her head.

"It's not the kind of uniforms that is causing the problem," Kirk said, feeling a little exasperated.

"Words don't need uniforms. Right, Kirk? Could Mother be confusing her vocabulary because all the words look alike?" Luke asked.

"That's what I'm thinking," Kirk agreed. "We had a problem with confused vocabulary before the uniforms. Remember?" Kirk removed *The Guide to Grammar Galaxy* from the shelf and found two articles that he read aloud.

Verb Confusion

The meaning of the verbs *lie/lay*, *sit/set*, *rise/raise*, and *can/may* are commonly confused. The difference between the first three verb pairs is similar: *Lie, sit,* and *rise* are intransitive verbs with no objects. *Lay, set,* and *raise* are transitive verbs that require an object of the action.

Some tricks to remember the difference are:

Lie = recline; lay = place. The word and its meaning have the same vowel sound.

A dog sits where you set his bowl.

You rise to raise your glass.

The past tense of these verbs can add to the confusion. See the chart below.

Present	Past
lie	lay
lay	laid
sit	sat
set	set
rise	rose
raise	raised

Can means to be able and *may* means to have permission. The game "Mother, May I?" can remind you that *may* means asking permission.

Incorrect

The cat laid down for a nap.   Raise up in protest.
Set yourself down for a rest.   Can I go over to my friend's house?

Commonly Confused Vocabulary

Some commonly confused vocabulary words can be differentiated by their part of speech, unique spelling, or specific meaning. Consult the chart below for words that are commonly misused. The highlighted words are homophones that are pronounced similarly, leading to confusion.

Commonly Confused Vocabulary Words					
Word	**Part of Speech; Meaning**	**Word**	**Part of Speech; Meaning**	**Word**	**Part of Speech; Meaning**
a lot	**Article, Noun;** many	**alot**	misspelling	**allot**	**Verb**; give as share; set apart
awhile	**Adv.;** done a short time	**a while**	**Noun**; period of time		
among	**Prep.;** amid 3 or more items not specified	**between**	**Prep.;** in the middle of 2 or more specific items		

Word	Part of Speech; Meaning	Word	Part of Speech; Meaning	Word	Part of Speech; Meaning
assure	**Verb**; tell to remove doubt	ensure	**Verb**; make certain	insure	**Verb**; provide security for
capital	**Noun**; city seat of government	capitol	**Noun**; legislative building		
complement	**Noun**; thing that completes **Verb**; make perfect	compliment	**Noun**; expression of praise **Verb**; commend		
emigrate	**Verb**; leave country to live elsewhere	immigrate	**Verb**; come to country to live		
historic	**Adj.**; important in history	historical	**Adj.**; about the past		
i.e.	**Abbrev.**; in other words	e.g.	**Abbrev.**; for example		
into	**Prep.**; indicates where	in to	**Adv., Prep.**; indicates purpose		
less	**Adj.**; used with uncountable nouns	fewer	**Adj.**; used with countable nouns		
login	**Noun**; process to gain computer access	log in	**Verb, Prep.**; start a computer or system session		
principal	**Noun**; school director	principle	**Noun**; value		
stationary	**Adj.**; immovable	stationery	**Noun**; printed paper		

Abbrev.= abbreviation; Adj.= adjective; Adv.= adverb; Prep.=preposition

"What can we do about these confused words on such short notice?" Ellen asked when Kirk finished reading.

"I'm going to have Father issue an emergency order to stop the wearing of uniforms," Kirk said.

"Good idea!" Luke enthused. "Do you think we should send out a mission on confused vocabulary words, too? I'd forgotten some of these differences," Luke said.

"You're suggesting a mission? I'm impressed," Ellen teased.

"I think Father will make us do it sooner or later anyway," Luke said, laughing.

Kirk contacted the king to explain and Luke and Ellen got to work on a Confused Vocabulary mission.

What does *histrionics* mean?

What is the difference between *emigrate* and *immigrate*?

What should the queen have said instead of: "I want to ensure you that bidding on any of these items promotes reading"?

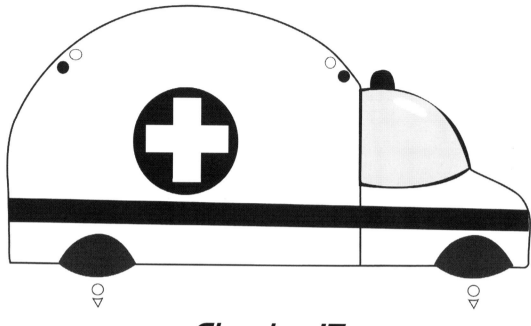

Chapter 15

"We're visiting Grandpa George this Saturday!" the queen announced enthusiastically.

"Is his hip completely healed?" Ellen asked.

"It is. He is getting around just fine now," the queen said.

"Good! Maybe we can play video golf or tennis with him then," Luke enthused.

"He'd like that," the queen said, smiling at the thought.

When the royal family arrived at Grandpa George's apartment, a voice they didn't recognize asked them to come in. Upon opening the door, they saw Grandpa George lying down with medical attendants examining him.

The queen was alarmed and rushed to her father's side. "What's wrong?" she asked breathlessly.

Before he could answer, the man who had a stethoscope on Grandpa George's chest explained. "We are EMTs. We got a call that your dad was experiencing tachycardia. We think it's a good idea for him to get an EKG. He has some peripheral edema that concerns me, too."

The queen replied tearfully. "I don't know what that is, but it sounds terrible. When did this happen?" she asked her father.

"There, there. Don't have a cow!" he told her. "It's not as heavy as it seems."

"You're feeling some heaviness in your chest?" the EMT asked.

"What? No!" Grandpa George said, irritated.

"Okay. We're going to have to take you to the hospital for some tests stat," the other EMT told him.

"What is a stat test?" the queen asked the EMT.

"That means right away, Mother," Ellen explained. "They say it on the medical show I watch."

"What medical show?" the queen asked, eyes narrowed. "You've been watching a show without permission?"

Ellen hung her head.

"We'll discuss that when we get home," the queen said sternly. Ellen nodded.

At the hospital, a nurse prepared Grandpa George for medical tests while the royal family sat in the waiting room.

"I'll need you to unbutton your shirt," the nurse told Grandpa George.

"10-4," he said, complying.

The nurse checked her watch. "It's later than 10. It's already afternoon," she replied.

"I know," Grandpa George said crossly. "Give me the skinny. How long will this take? I want to spend time with my family."

"I can get you a diet soda after we do the test. It shouldn't be more than an hour," the nurse responded.

"I don't drink diet soda. Do me a solid then. Let's get it done quickly."

"If you want it done quickly, you'll need to wait for solids until after the test," the nurse said, beginning to be annoyed with her patient. "I'm going to put these electrodes on your chest now, okay?" the nurse explained.

"You're going to shock my heart? My heart is already beating. You'll kill me!" he said, shouting.

"Okay, sir. Calm down. I won't put the electrodes on. I'm going to talk to your family. Just relax," she said, smiling to reassure him.

In the waiting room, the nurse **addressed** the queen. "I'm wondering about your father's mental **capacity**," she began.

"Capacity for what?" the queen asked.

"He seems confused," she replied. "Does he have a history of MI?"

"MI?" the queen repeated.

Ellen interjected. "Has he ever had a heart attack?"

"No," the queen answered curtly.

"Also, does he have a DNR in place?" the nurse asked.

"I'm not sure what medical equipment they have at his place," the queen said. "I can call them."

The queen picked up her communicator when Ellen explained. "A DNR is a Do Not **Resuscitate** order. It means if he stops breathing, he doesn't want extreme measures taken to bring him back."

"Stop breathing? Has he stopped breathing?" the queen shrieked, jumping up from her seat.

"No, no. He's fine!" the nurse said. "We just like to have the patient's wishes on record in case anything happens."

"Are you trying to give *me* a heart attack? Would you just do the tests so we can take him home?" the queen pleaded.

"I'm going to need some help keeping him calm," the nurse said.

"I can do it. I know a lot of medical terms, and I know how Grandpa talks," Ellen said.

"Hm. I'm still not happy that you've been watching that show. But you might be able to keep Grandpa calm. Okay. Thank you, Ellen," the queen said, squeezing her daughter's hand.

When Ellen and the nurse left the waiting room, the king put his arm around his wife. "I think we've had a vocabulary issue."

"Not now, dear. Galaxy business can wait until we know my father is okay," the queen said, pulling away from him.

"I *was* talking about your father. I think slang and jargon were upsetting him and you, too."

"I remember that mission. We thought Grandpa had dementia because he was talking funny. But it was because he was using vocabulary from his generation," Luke said.

76

"That's right, Luke," the king said.

"I don't remember learning much medical jargon for that mission," Kirk said. "Maybe we can prevent miscommunication for other families by having the guardians complete a mission that includes terms medical professionals know and the rest of us don't."

"That's a splendid idea, Kirk. You can ask one of the staff members for definitions of medical jargon to send," the king said.

The two boys used the wait to prepare a mission on slang and jargon.

What does *resuscitate* mean?

What is medical jargon?

Why was Grandpa George getting upset with the nurse?

Chapter 16

"Have you decided what project you'll be working on for the Galaxy Science Fair?" the king asked his children at breakfast.

"Yes! We agreed on a topic. That's amazing!" Ellen said, laughing.

"We're doing a project on star life cycles," Kirk said.

"Oh, what a great topic. I can't wait to see the finished project," the king enthused.

"You're not going to **procrastinate**, are you?" the queen asked suspiciously.

"We'll let you know next week," Luke joked.

Everyone laughed.

★ ★ ★ ★ ★ ★ ★ ★ ★

procrastinate – *delay*

intertwined – *together*

cavalier – *inconsiderate*

★ ★ ★ ★ ★ ★ ★ ★ ★

The following week, the queen checked on her children's progress. She found them arguing in the art studio.

"Hey! What's happening here? Pull yourself together and tell me what the problem is," she said.

The children huddled together, arms **intertwined**. "We can't decide the format to use for the project," Ellen said over her shoulder.

"Does huddling together like that help you decide?" the queen asked, eyebrows raised.

"I don't know. We hadn't tried it until you came in," Ellen said, dropping her arms and taking a step back.

"What formats are you considering?" the queen asked.

"I can tell you. To make a long story short," Luke began. "Once upon a time, the end."

"What? Don't be **cavalier** about this, Luke," the queen warned.

"I want to build a model. Ellen thought that would be too complicated, but I told her it's not rocket science," Kirk said.

"T minus 90 seconds and counting. All systems are go," an announcer said.

78

"Luke, that isn't funny," the queen warned.

"I know. I didn't say it. Must have been my communicator," Luke replied. "I want to use video in the project."

"And I told him I didn't want to cut corners with this project," Ellen said.

Luke began cutting the corners off a piece of cardstock.

"What are you doing?" the queen asked him.

"Working on the project!" Luke replied defensively. Ellen grimaced in frustration. "The problem is Ellen keeps getting bent out of shape," he added.

Ellen began stretching on the floor. "Now what are *you* doing?" the queen asked her.

"I'm trying to relax. Working with these two is so stressful!" Ellen complained.

"Well, hang in there. You'll work it out," the queen said, smiling to encourage her. Then she saw Ellen hanging upside down from a rafter. "What on English are you doing now?" she asked.

"Stretching my back," Ellen explained.

"Something is definitely wrong," the queen declared.

"You can say that again," Luke replied.

"Something is definitely wrong," the queen repeated. "Why did I say that again?"

"I think I know. Remember when idioms were moved from Idiom Island and crazy things like this started happening?" Kirk said.

"What's an idiom again?" Ellen asked, down from the rafter.

"It's an expression that means something other than its words indicate," Kirk replied.

"Right. So what's happening in the galaxy to make these idioms literal?" Ellen asked.

Kirk used his communicator to get a status report on Idiom Island.

Screen replied, "Idioms are being evacuated due to a hurricane expected to hit the island."

"Where are they being transported?" Kirk asked.

"Nonfiction Province."

Kirk groaned. "We have to get them out of there."

"And send them where?" Ellen asked.

"We'll cross that bridge when we come to it," Kirk said, regretting it as a bridge appeared in front of them.

"Cool," Luke whispered. "Can we walk on it? Or is it an illusion?"

"Ignore it and it will go away," Kirk said sternly. "The top priority is getting the guardians' help with this crisis. We'll need help identifying the expressions that need to be transported."

His siblings agreed and got to work on an idioms mission.

What does *cavalier* mean?

What is an idiom?

Why were idioms being literally experienced?

Chapter 17

"Ellen, I was speaking with Mrs. **Fastidious** today. She said she'd like to hire you as a mother's helper one day a week. Are you interested?"

★ ★ ★ ★ ★ ★ ★ ★ ★ ★ ★

fastidious – *very careful*

★ ★ ★ ★ ★ ★ ★ ★ ★ ★ ★

"How many kids does she have? Not triplets, I hope," Ellen joked.

"No," the queen said, laughing. "And not babies. They're two younger children. She wants you to play with them so she can get some work done."

"Okay. I could do that," Ellen said, smiling.

"Thank you, Ellen. She'll be thrilled," the queen said, preparing to contact her.

The following week, Ellen was welcomed to Mrs. Fastidious's home. She met the two children she would be supervising: Layla, who was four and Carter, who was two.

"This is Ellen. She will be playing any games you want to play and will be giving you a healthy snack. I'll be working and will be here if you need me, but I don't like to be interrupted," Mrs. Fastidious explained. She smiled at Ellen and showed her around the house, with Carter and Layla following **inquisitively**.

★ ★ ★ ★ ★ ★ ★ ★ ★ ★

inquisitively – *curiously*

★ ★ ★ ★ ★ ★ ★ ★ ★ ★

"We're going to have fun, aren't we?" Ellen asked them, crouching down to their level. Layla immediately burst into tears. Carter screamed.

"They just need time to get to know you," Mrs. Fastidious said over the screaming.

Ellen's eyes grew wide with panic as she watched Mrs. Fastidious leave the room. *It could be as bad as watching the triplets*, she worried.

Before she had time to worry more, Layla brought her a balancing-block game. "Play with me!" she demanded.

"Okay," Ellen said, unsure whether to be annoyed or relieved. Ellen organized the pieces and the colored die on the table.

Layla rolled the die and got yellow. She carefully placed a small yellow block on the wooden moon. Ellen rolled a red and placed a large red block on the opposite end.

Carter stood behind Layla, watching them play. Ellen was relieved that he was being quiet.

Layla rolled a blue. She carefully added a blue block next to the yellow one.

"Good job!" Ellen said.

"I'm going to win," Layla boasted.

Play continued for a few minutes until several blocks were positioned precariously on the moon. Carter lunged forward and lifted one end of it, scattering the blocks.

Layla trembled, balled her fists, and screamed in rage. She chased Carter around the room. He laughed until Layla caught him and began beating him with her fists. Then Carter screamed.

Ellen pulled Layla off Carter just as Mrs. Fastidious entered the room.

"Ellen!" Mrs. Fastidious said sharply, her face flushed. "I am glad you and the children are having fun. But I thought I made it clear that I wasn't to be disturbed. You cannot be screaming while I'm working."

Ellen was flabbergasted. She wanted to explain, but the expression on Mrs. Fastidious's face said that she wasn't open to hearing it. Instead, Ellen mumbled an okay.

When she left, it was Ellen's turn to tremble. This wasn't going well.

"I want a snack," Layla whined.

"Uh, okay," Ellen said weakly.

The two children followed Ellen into the kitchen, where she removed the fruit and yogurt from the refrigerator. As she put them on the table, Layla followed behind her with packaged snacks in hand.

"Here, Carter," she said in a sing-song voice. "It's your favorite."

Carter squealed with delight as he took the chips and candy from Layla.

"Your mother wanted you to have the fruit," Ellen said, frowning.

"Well, we want this," Layla said, opening a package of candy, challenging her.

Ellen reached for the package of chips in Carter's hand.

"He'll scream if you take it away," Layla said, smirking.

Ellen didn't know what to do. She decided to interrupt Mrs. Fastidious and ask her.

When she saw Ellen at her office door, Mrs. Fastidious was sure one of the children was injured and she was frantic.

"No, no, they're fine. It's just that, they want candy and chips and if I don't give it to them, they'll scream," Ellen said.

Mrs. Fastidious relaxed. "Is that all?" she asked, exasperated.

Ellen looked at the floor. "Yes," she said quietly.

"I'll have you clean up the snack when they're done. Will you be able to manage for the rest of the time that you're scheduled?" she asked impatiently.

Ellen nodded and returned to the kitchen, feeling conflicting emotions. Layla smiled smugly as she reported that they were too full to eat the fruit.

Ellen did her best to keep the kids quiet the rest of the afternoon.

When her mother rang the bell to get her, Ellen nearly ran out the door. Mrs. Fastidious thanked the queen for bringing Ellen over. The queen didn't linger as she wanted to catch up with Ellen. She could tell something was wrong.

"Are you okay?" she asked when she reached her.

"Yes. No. I don't know!" she wailed as she walked.

"Okay. Tell me what happened," the queen said after stopping her.

"The kids are bad," Ellen said.

"What do you mean 'bad'?" the queen asked.

"I don't know. Their behavior is very bad!" Ellen said quickly.

"As in **incorrigible**?" the queen asked.

★ ★ ★ ★ ★ ★ ★ ★ ★ ★

incorrigible – *beastly*

★ ★ ★ ★ ★ ★ ★ ★ ★ ★

"If that means very bad behavior, then yes!" Ellen said, continuing to walk.

"Did you talk to Mrs. Fastidious about it?" the queen asked, walking to keep up with her.

Ellen laughed bitterly. "Yes. Let's just say she was not very helpful."

"What do you mean, 'not very helpful'?"

"You don't understand," Ellen said. She shook her head in frustration and wiped away a tear.

The queen sighed and side hugged her daughter. "I'm sorry you're upset," the queen said.

"I'm more than upset," Ellen said. "And I'm not going back."

As soon as the two arrived home, the queen found the king to talk about Ellen's reaction to babysitting.

"I have a very big problem with Ellen after her babysitting job today. She says I don't understand. But she only describes what happened as the kids being 'very bad' and Mrs. Fastidious as being 'not very helpful.'"

"I know what's wrong," the king said.

"You do? Did Ellen call you while she was babysitting?" the queen asked, surprised by his reaction.

"No. We have a very big problem in Synonym City. Vocabulary words that can be defined with the word *very* are being evicted."

The queen gasped. "What? Why?"

"The Gremlin's propaganda has the mayor convinced that the city is very crowded. Without these synonyms, we have no shades of meaning. We just have *bad* and *very bad*, for example," the king explained.

"What are you going to do?" the queen asked.

"I'm going to order the evictions halted very soon. Then I'm going to have the guardians help us put evicted vocabulary words back with their synonyms."

"That's a very good plan. I'll wait to talk to Ellen about her babysitting experience until the synonyms are back home."

What does *incorrigible* mean in the story?

What is required to have shades of meaning?

Why does the queen want to wait to talk to Ellen?

Chapter 18

"I think we should plan a beach vacation over the holidays this year," the queen announced as the family sat down for dinner.

"Beach vacations are far too expensive," the king said, shaking his head.

"How do you know? We have never researched one," the queen said, **miffed** by his response.

"Ernie went on a beach vacation with his wife, and he has a lot of money," the king answered.

"That's a red herring," Kirk said.

★ ★ ★ ★ ★ ★ ★ ★ ★

miffed – *annoyed*

fallacy – *error*

erroneous – *mistaken*

★ ★ ★ ★ ★ ★ ★ ★ ★

"Where?" Luke asked, looking around. "Are we having fish for dinner?"

Kirk laughed. "No, a red herring isn't just a fish. It's a logical **fallacy**. Father used a red herring in his argument."

"What?" the king said, his voice rising. "There is nothing **erroneous** about what I said."

"A red herring can be true, but it doesn't support your argument. It's a distraction and not relevant," Kirk explained.

"Thank you, Kirk," the queen said, smirking at the king.

"So, are we going to the beach?" Ellen asked, eyes shining.

"Kirk, where did you learn about red herrings?" the king asked, ignoring her.

"I'm studying logic to prepare for a test I'm required to take. I can't take an advanced course in robotics unless I score well enough on the logic test," Kirk explained.

"So, I can expect you to continue to defeat my arguments and cost me money then," the king joked. Everyone laughed.

The next morning at breakfast, the king was complaining about a newspaper article. "Listen to this!" he said before reading a quote. "'The king argues that keeping as many vocabulary words as possible in circulation is good for the galaxy. But he is middle-aged and too old-fashioned to be forming vocabulary policy.' I'm not old. This is preposterous! Everyone tells me I look ten years younger than I am," the king said, defending himself.

"That's an ad hominem fallacy," Kirk stated.

"It's a logical fallacy that I look ten years younger than I am?" the king said, getting frustrated.

"No, no," Kirk said, trying to calm him. "The reporter used an ad hominem attack in the article. Instead of discussing your vocabulary policy, the article attacked you personally. The fact that you're middle-aged doesn't mean you don't have a good policy."

"The *fact* that I'm middle aged?" the king groaned. "So, you're saying I should have this reporter fired for attacking me personally?"

Kirk responded quickly. "No! People use ad hominem arguments all the time. It's bad reasoning but not worthy of firing. In my opinion," he added to placate him.

"Okay. I won't throw him into the dungeon then," the king said. "I was kidding about having him fired." He smiled at Kirk, who swiped his brow in mock relief. "You seem to be learning a lot and should do well on your logic test," the king said.

Several weeks later, Kirk was downcast as he sat in the sunroom, communicator in hand.

"What is it, Kirk?" the king asked.

"I failed the logic test," he said glumly.

"What? I can't believe it. You studied so hard," the king said.

"I did. But I didn't tell you about the test."

"What about it?" the king asked.

"It had nothing about logic on it. It was all these problems with the double colons."

"Double colons? Oh, you mean analogies?" the king asked.

"Yes, analogies. I know we studied them before."

"Analogies require a form of logical reasoning. Did the analogies use word pairs?" the king asked.

"Yes," Kirk said, sighing. "It had questions like *assuredly* is to *hesitantly* as *befitting* is to what? I knew I had messed up as soon as I saw the first problem."

"Kirk, word analogies test your logical reasoning as applied to vocabulary. You have to remember synonyms, antonyms, and shades of meaning. You have an excellent vocabulary, and you should have passed the test. But you allowed your expectations to get in the way."

When Kirk seemed confused, the king continued. "You expected questions on logical fallacies. When you saw analogies, you told yourself that you weren't prepared and wouldn't do well on the test, right?" Kirk nodded. "What should you do now?"

"Write an analogies mission?" Kirk asked.

The king smiled. "That's a great idea, but I mean for the robotics course."

"I can't take it now that I've failed the logic test."

"Are you sure about that?" the king asked. "Is there an option to take the test again? If not, when will the course be offered next? Guardians don't fail to complete a mission and then quit."

Kirk thought for a moment. "I don't know. But you're right! I'm going to look into my options right away. Thanks, Father!" Kirk said gratefully.

"When you know your next step, ask your brother and sister to help you write an analogies mission," the king said.

What does *fallacy* mean?

What do word analogies test?

Why did Kirk fail the analogies test?

Unit IV: Adventures in Grammar

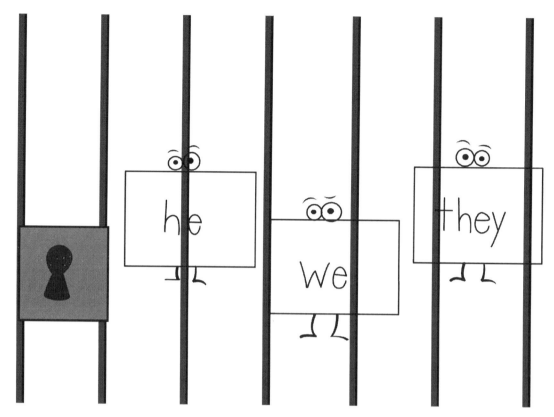

Chapter 19

The king saw the headline before he reached the newspaper on the dining room table: Crime Ring Bust on Planet Sentence. He strode quickly to the table and began scanning the article.

"The Major Case Squad reports that some pronouns on planet Sentence **colluded** to dominate English grammar. The subjects of the investigation have been arrested. The planet's prosecutor hasn't commented on whether or not she will put them on trial. But a staffer in the prosecutor's office told us that there is **ample** evidence of fraud."

★ ★ ★ ★ ★ ★ ★ ★ ★ ★

colluded – *plotted*

ample – *plentiful*

★ ★ ★ ★ ★ ★ ★ ★ ★ ★

"What on English? How can pronouns be criminals?" the king asked out loud.

"What's happening, dear?" the queen asked as she came to the table.

The king explained the article to her, then ate his breakfast in a hurry. He wanted to get the details from the prosecutor herself.

"Hello, Your Majesty," the prosecutor greeted the king warmly.

"Hello. I don't believe we have met yet. Unfortunately, we don't have time for small talk. I want to know what's happening with the pronouns. I don't understand how they can be guilty of fraud," the king said.

"It's always hard to believe that people we trusted could violate that trust," she said in an **imperious** tone.

★ ★ ★ ★ ★ ★ ★ ★ ★

imperious – *arrogant*

★ ★ ★ ★ ★ ★ ★ ★ ★

"Right," the king said slowly, "but pronouns aren't people."

"They have desires just like people, and sometimes those desires lead them to make bad choices. That's what happened in this case," the prosecutor said confidently.

The king was so astonished that he was speechless for a moment.

"We haven't formally pressed charges yet, but when we do, I'm sure you'll be briefed on the details," she said. "Is there anything else I can help you with today?" she said with a forced smile.

"No," the king said woodenly. After he'd disconnected, he thought of plenty to say. His temper flared as he considered her attitude.

When he heard a knock on his study door, he barked, "Come in!"

It was the queen, who grimaced at his volume. "Your conversation must not have gone well," she said sympathetically.

"No, no, it didn't," the king said, standing up and beginning to pace. "I don't know any more about the pronouns' arrest than I did before."

"Me am sorry," the queen said, patting her husband's arm.

The king stopped pacing. "What did you say?" he asked.

"Me said me am sorry," the queen replied tentatively. She hoped to settle the king down. "Her didn't explain what's going on?"

"Her?" the king asked.

"The prosecutor is a woman, yes?"

"Yes," the king said slowly.

"Okay. But her didn't tell you what the charges are," the queen said.

The king shook his head no and thanked his wife for her support.

"You are welcome. Me know you will get the problem solved," she said, smiling.

The king sighed with relief when he ushered her out of the room. He had a good idea which pronouns had been arrested, but he wanted to be sure. He contacted Grammar Patrol headquarters on planet Sentence.

"Hello! Need some information on the pronoun prisoners," the king said when the captain joined the call.

"All right. What do you want to know?" the captain asked.

"Need to know which pronouns are in custody."

The captain looked down at a tablet and scanned a document. "*I, he, she, we,* and *they,*" he said.

"Not *you,*" the king said to clarify.

The captain frowned. "Of course not. Just pronouns in the crime ring."

"*It* is not in custody either," the king stated to confirm.

"Didn't say *it,*" the captain replied.

"You didn't say *it* was in custody?" the king asked.

"Right. Are us finished?" the captain asked impatiently.

"Uh, yes," the king said, realizing there was no point to continuing the conversation.

When he ended the call, he started worrying. The subject pronouns that weren't also used as object pronouns were in jail and unavailable for use. If the pronouns had been convicted of a crime, he could pardon them and have them released. But while they were still in the justice system, he could do nothing.

He had to give the Gremlin credit. This was a brilliant way to confuse people's grammar. *The prosecutor must be working with him,* the king thought. Then he had an idea. He would hire a defense attorney to get the pronouns released on bail. The attorney could use the guardians' testimony of the essential work that these pronouns do.

He found Kirk, Luke, and Ellen and explained the situation. The three of them agreed to write a mission called Subject vs. Object Pronouns.

What does *imperious* mean?

What is an object pronoun that wasn't in custody?

Why was the king relieved when the queen left his study?

Chapter 20

The king threw down his newspaper in disgust. "The prosecutor is going forward with the case against the subject pronouns."

"You're kidding," the queen said.

"I wish."

"What will happen next?" she asked.

"The paper said that the prosecution will make its case by calling other pronouns to testify."

"How can pronouns testify?" she asked.

"Exactly," the king sighed. "This trial will be a **sham**, but there's nothing I can do about it."

"Don't worry, dear. Justice will **prevail**," the queen said confidently.

★ ★ ★ ★ ★ ★ ★ ★ ★

sham – *phony*

prevail – *triumph*

proprietors – *owners*

★ ★ ★ ★ ★ ★ ★ ★ ★

Several weeks later, the pronouns' trial was being aired across the galaxy. Cook and the children joined the king and queen in the media room to watch.

The prosecutor addressed the jury in her opening remarks. "These pronouns were the subject of a year-long investigation," she said, gesturing to *I*, *he*, *she*, *we*, and *they*. What that investigation uncovered has shocked us all. That these words would seek to eliminate the competition and become the sole **proprietors** of sentences is hard to believe. Even our own king doubted the depths of their evil intentions. But yes, ladies and gentlemen of the jury, these words did conspire to overthrow their fellow pronouns. Their next target was the monarchy itself." The spectators gasped.

The king rolled his eyes. "I doubted it because I don't believe they did anything wrong."

The prosecutor called the interrogative pronouns to the witness stand. The word *what* represented them. "Tell me about the time you were the subject of the sentence and *I* stole your place," she said.

"I object!" the defense attory said.

Before the judge could respond, the prosecutor spoke. "This is exactly what happened. It was *what*'s turn and *I* interjected."

The judge paused and looked worriedly at the camera. "Overruled?" he said as a question more than a statement.

"I have no more questions," the prosecutor said abruptly. "Your witness," she told the defender.

The defense attorney asked the witness when this had occurred.

"What?" the pronoun said.

Raising his volume, the attorney repeated the question.

"What?" the pronoun repeated.

The attorney sighed. "I have no more questions."

"What are the interrogative pronouns again?" Luke asked.

"*Who, whom, which,* and *what,*" Ellen replied.

"Okay," Luke said, frowning. "Who, whom, which, and what are the interrogative pronouns?"

"Ugh. Just watch the trial," Ellen groaned.

"I call the demonstrative pronouns to the stand," the prosecutor said. The pronoun *these* took its place near the judge. "You too suffered at the hands of subject pronouns. Would you please indicate which pronouns violently took your place in a sentence?"

"These," the word said.

"Let the record show that the witness has identified the defendants," the prosecutor said smugly.

"Before you ask, Luke, the demonstrative pronouns are *this, that, these,* and *those,*" Ellen said.

"Where are you pointing? I don't see them," Luke complained.

"Quiet, you two," the queen said. "The defense attorney isn't questioning these, so the prosecutor is calling the reflexive pronouns to the stand."

The word *ourselves* took its place next to the judge. "Before you give your testimony about the appalling behavior of the subject pronouns, tell me on whose behalf you are speaking," the prosecutor said.

"Ourselves," the word replied.

"After experiencing the abuse firsthand, who will suffer if we don't find the defendants guilty?"

"Ourselves," the word repeated.

"Objection! Improper grammar," the defense attorney cried.

"Your honor, are we really going to demand proper grammar from a witness?" the prosecutor said in a supercilious tone.

The judge's eyes grew wide as he stared at the camera. "Overruled," he said less than confidently.

"The reflexive pronouns are *myself, oneself, yourself, yourselves, himself, herself, itself, themselves*, and *ourselves*," Kirk said. "I remember how painful it was when they were the subject of a documentary."

The defense attorney declined to question *ourselves*, so it was excused. The prosecutor called indefinite pronouns to the stand. The word *all* took its place to be questioned.

The prosector asked which of the subject pronouns were guilty of illegal behavior.

"All," the word said.

When it was the defense attorney's turn to question the word, he asked, "Which of the subject pronouns can you replace in a sentence?"

"All," it said.

"Are you sure? Let the record show that the witness claims it can take the place of both singular and plural subject pronouns, when it is indefinite. Take the sentence 'He wins.' *He* is singular. *All* cannot replace *he* in the sentence. 'All wins' is incorrect."

"Objection, Your Honor. The indefinite pronoun *all* can be singular or plural," the prosecutor said, rising to her feet.

"That is true, but in this case, *all* cannot replace *he*," the defense attorney said, smiling victoriously.

The judge rubbed his temple, grimacing in pain. "We are going to take a short recess," he said, hitting his gavel on the desk.

The royal family had just begun discussing the case when the king was alerted that the defense attorney was waiting to talk with him via video. The king thought it would be fine for the rest of the family to listen, so he took the call on the media-room screen.

"I have an idea," the attorney said, shifting side to side with excitement. "I want the guardians to help me prove that the case against the subject pronouns should be thrown out."

"How?" the king asked.

"Their mission on subject pronouns helped me get the words out on bail. Could they complete another mission on pronouns that I can use as evidence in court?" the attorney asked.

"I don't see why not. We will get to work on it right away," the king promised.

The attorney thanked him and the three children worked on an emergency mission on indefinite and other pronouns.

What does *prevail* mean?

What are the demonstrative pronouns?

Why can't indefinite pronouns replace subject pronouns?

Chapter 21

The king was eager to read his Op Ed in the **conservative** newspaper *The Guardian*. He wrote about the principles that create a strong galaxy, like a commitment to reading, writing, and good grammar. He knew the paper's editor would be in full agreement with what he wrote. The editor opposed the Gremlin even more than he did. The king had even had to insist that banishing the Gremlin from the galaxy wasn't an option. Chuckling about that, the king paged to the article and read the first paragraphs.

★ ★ ★ ★ ★ ★ ★ ★ ★ ★

conservative – *traditional*

★ ★ ★ ★ ★ ★ ★ ★ ★ ★

The galaxy is strong. Because of our Guardian Program, more kids read than ever. Our librarians tell me that circulation of all genres of books has increased.

Writing skill has improved, too. Children write thank-you notes and letters, but they also write stories, articles, and even full-length books.

The king was used to having his work edited, especially by **liberal** publications that wanted fewer grammar rules. Even though his article was in *The Guardian*, something about it seemed different. He couldn't figure out what it was, though, so he went to find the original article in his study.

★ ★ ★ ★ ★ ★ ★ ★ ★ ★

liberal – *reformist*

exultant – *joyful*

★ ★ ★ ★ ★ ★ ★ ★ ★ ★

The galaxy is strong. Because of our Guardian Program, more kids are reading than ever. Our librarians tell me that circulation of all genres of books has been increasing.

Writing skills have been improving, too. Children are writing thank-you notes and letters, but they are also writing stories, articles, and even full-length books.

The same content, but the tense had been changed. Specifically, the progressive tense had been eliminated. Why the change, he wondered, when his verion seemed better.

He shrugged and concluded it didn't matter. Trying to understand editors' choices was foolishness, he told himself with a grin. He continued reading the article in the paper.

Immediately, he found another instance of the progressive tense being removed. He had to admit, it irked him. He knew he shouldn't, but he placed a call to the editor of *The Guardian.*

"Hey, Joel!" the king said in a phony **exultant** greeting.

"Hello, Your Majesty!" the editor said. "I take it you got the paper. We loved publishing your article this week. You're making a strong case for traditional grammar. As you know, we believe that's a cause worth fighting for." He smiled broadly and waited for the king to agree.

"Yes, I like having *The Guardian* as an ally," the king said haltingly.

"You can count on us, Sire," the editor said, pulling his shoulders back and sitting a little taller.

"Wonderful, wonderful," the king said, clearly distracted. "Say, I noticed the edits on my article," he began.

"Oh, yes. You know we aren't correcting errors. It's a stylistic choice," the editor said casually.

"Stylistic?"

"Yes, we don't want to show support for the progressives in our paper," he explained.

"Progressives. You don't want your paper to be perceived as liberal by your readers?" the king summarized.

"Exactly," the editor said, pleased that the king understood.

"You realize, though, that the progressive tense has nothing to do with politics," the king said slowly.

"Grammar always has something to do with politics," the editor insisted, taking a serious tone.

"Joel, the progressive tense has been used for generations. It's just a way of showing that a verb's action is in progress and ongoing," the king said a little tersely.

"Right. That's how we lose the galaxy—one little compromise at a time. At *The Guardian*, we are making sure that grammar is still good for our children and our grandchildren. I know you agree."

"Uh, right," the king said, his shoulders drooping. "Anyway, thank you for publishing the article."

"Any time, Your Majesty," the editor said, beaming.

The king was relieved to end the call. The whole idea of rejecting the progressive tense bothered him. Yet he doubted that he would change Joel's mind, no matter how he explained it. He wanted to talk it over with the queen. She was good at sorting out relationship issues.

After he'd explained the situation, she affirmed his conclusion. "He isn't open to hearing the facts. You're right to let it go. But I know people who are open to hearing the facts."

"Who?"

"The guardians. That's why we have them, isn't it? They're being trained to know grammar and use it correctly regardless of politics," she explained.

"You're right," the king said, relieved.

"I usually am," she quipped.

The king laughed, then pondered. "The progressive tense can be challenging. I think the children should send out a refresher mission on it. I know Joel has kids who are guardians," he said mischievously.

The queen smiled at his plan.

What does *exultant* mean?

What is the progressive tense?

Why didn't the editor want the progressive tense in *The Guardian*?

Chapter 22

"I'm so excited. Mel Wright is going to be speaking this weekend," the queen told her husband as they got ready for bed.

"Who's Mel Wright?" he asked.

"Only the most motivational speaker ever," the queen said playfully.

The king groaned. "Not another motivational speaker. Last time you saw one it was a disaster."

"You're exaggerating as usual. This speaker is a woman who will inspire me to live my best life."

"You're already living your best life because you're married to me," the king teased. "I know you'll want to make changes when you come home. I just hope none of them affect me."

The queen laughed and then tried to sleep despite her enthusiasm.

That weekend, the queen was in an auditorium full of women who were as thrilled to hear Mel as she was. They didn't take special notice of her as queen, and she was glad. She wanted to focus on Mel's message.

The women rose to their feet and applauded when Mel took the stage. "Thank you. Thank you for that warm welcome," she said.

★ ★ ★ ★ ★ ★ ★ ★ ★ ★

subsided – *decreased*

★ ★ ★ ★ ★ ★ ★ ★ ★ ★

After the applause **subsided**, Mel explained what the attendees could expect from the evening. "You're here because you want to be the best version of yourself. I'm going to help you, but my method may surprise you. I'm going to teach you a little grammar tonight." Some of the women groaned. Others laughed.

"It will be painless, I promise," she joked. "The fact is that what we accomplish in life is impacted by our mood. Am I right?" Women were nodding and saying yes.

"I'm glad we agree on that. You may not remember learning that there are moods in grammar." A few women expressed surprise and asked those sitting next to them if they remembered.

"There are moods in grammar," Mel continued, "and I'm going to use them to help you crush your goals this year." Several women clapped.

"Let's start with the interrogative mood." A question mark appeared on the large screen behind Mel. "The interrogative mood asks a question. It uses helping verb forms of *be*, *do*, *is*, and *have*. I have some questions for you. Who are you going to be when you leave here?" She paused dramatically. "What are you going to do when you leave here? What is going to be your big goal? When will you know that you have reached it?"

The women murmured and the queen was thinking deeply about her responses.

Mel continued. "When you've answered those questions, you're ready to move from the interrogative mood to the imperative mood. The imperative mood issues a command. The subject of the command is *you*, but it's often not specified. Let me be clear. *I'm* not commanding you to do anthing," she said. Then she gestured to the audience. "You're taking command of your life now. You're going to say, 'Sit down and write that book. When you're done writing, start getting rid of the clutter that's holding you back.'" More women applauded this time, including the queen.

"But let's be honest. You've given yourselves commands before, haven't you. And you didn't follow through because of a problem with your indicative mood. The indicative mood makes statements of facts or belief. If you've failed to reach your goals, I can almost guarantee it's because you've stated your negative beliefs about yourself as though they're facts. 'I'm not talented enough to write. I'm a procrastinator.' Raise your hand if you've been believing you're not enough!" Nearly every hand was raised.

"My friends, we have to stop believing lies about ourselves. Raise your hand if you're a writer!" A few women tentatively raised their hands until Mel encouraged them. "That's right! Now raise your hand if you're organized." She got the same tentative response until she cheered them on.

"We only need these three grammatical moods. If we limited ourselves to them, we would achieve more than we dreamed possible. Oops! I just used the **constraining** conditional mood. This is one of the moods that kills our goals. 'When I have time off, I should work on my book. If my kids helped me, I would get organized.' Ladies, this is **defeatist** thinking."

★ ★ ★ ★ ★ ★ ★ ★ ★

constraining – *limiting*

defeatist – *negative*

★ ★ ★ ★ ★ ★ ★ ★ ★

Murmurs of agreement were heard around the auditorium.

"The second mood that keeps us stuck is subjunctive. It's the worst mood of them all. It uses the third-person form of the verb without the -s ending. And it uses *be* rather than *is/are*. When describing a wish or a possibility, it uses *were* instead of *was*.

"And get this...the subjunctive mood expresses a wish for something that may not be possible. May not be possible? The subjuctive mood is killing your dreams. 'If I were a writer, I would share my ideas. If she were motivated, she could accomplish great things.' Ladies, it's time to get our grammatical moods under control! It won't happen until we get the conditional and subjunctive moods out of our galaxy for good."

Women stood to applaud. The queen hesitated for a moment but joined them. She knew she could accomplish so much more without these limits.

Mel had women who had been successful by eliminating these moods join her on stage. Their stories and Mel's message had the queen and the other attendees inspired and ready to change their lives.

As they left, each woman was asked to sign a petition demanding the elimination of the conditional and subjunctive moods from the galaxy. The queen shook her head and brushed past the staff people holding the petition. On her way home, she tried not to let a nagging concern about the petition take away from the emotional high she was experiencing.

"How was it?" the king asked her with a hug when she arrived home.

"Amazing!" the queen gushed. "She is so inspiring."

"What big changes are you going to make?" he asked warmly.

"For one, I'm going to believe that I'm a writer and I *will* get my next book done."

"Good for you!"

"And I'm going to get this house organized," she said firmly.

"I think you're pretty organized already, but okay," he said.

"And I'm going to stop using the conditional and subjunctive mood. They're holding me back," she said, carefully watching the king's response.

He laughed, but the queen frowned. "Oh, you're serious," he said.

"Yes, I'm serious! We all are. Mel had everyone sign a petition to ban these moods from the galaxy," she said, challenging him.

"Tell me you didn't sign it," the king said tersely.

"I didn't, but I should have," she said defiantly.

"Why on English would you believe that grammatical moods are a problem?" he said too loudly. When he saw his wife's reaction, he calmed himself. "Wait a minute. This makes no sense unless Mel Wright is being influenced by the Gremlin."

"You think everyone is working with the Gremlin," the queen said.

"No, just people who try to destroy the English language," he said defensively.

The queen's eyes blazed and she abruptly left for their bedchamber.

"I knew seeing a motivational speaker was a bad idea," he said to himself, sighing.

But the next morning, he apologized. "I was insensitive. I spoiled your excitement. I also shouldn't have assumed that Mel is working with the Gremlin."

The queen hugged him. "Thank you, dear. But you were right."

The king's mouth hung open. "What?"

"I couldn't sleep last night because of our discussion. I thought it was because I was upset with you, but it was because Mel's focus on grammatical mood was bothering me. I started reading through her social media posts. She has been outspoken about her belief that grammar doesn't matter. And get this...she's even been critical of you. That crosses the line," she said sternly.

The king hugged her. "I have the best wife in the galaxy. You don't need to change a thing about yourself."

"Oh, but I do. I'm going to make sure people know the truth about grammatical mood, beginning with the guardians," she said.

"The kids are sending out a mission?" he asked.

She nodded and kissed the king on the cheek before going to find the children.

What does *constraining* mean?

What are the five grammatical moods?

Why was the queen angry about the king's concerns about Mel Wright?

Chapter 23

"The Film Festival is coming up this weekend and I can't wait to go!" Luke enthused at dinner.

"We haven't agreed to go, have we, dear?" the king asked the queen.

"I don't know anything about it," the queen said absentmindedly.

"They're releasing new adventure films at the festival, rather than in theaters. By going, we will be the first to see these movies," Luke explained.

Luke responded to the king's **dispassionate** expression. "They're going to have the new *Star Journey* movie there," he

★ ★ ★ ★ ★ ★ ★ ★ ★ ★

dispassionate – *unemotional*

sing-song – *rising & falling*

★ ★ ★ ★ ★ ★ ★ ★ ★ ★

said in a **sing-song** voice to entice him.

"Hm. *Star Journey*, eh? Kirk, would you like to go?" the king asked. "It could be a fun family trip."

"I'll go," Kirk said eagerly.

"I'd like to go, too," the queen agreed.

"Mmm. I'm not a *Star Journey* fan," Ellen said, frowning.

"But we'd all be going," the king said.

Ellen shook her head. "I don't want to," she insisted.

Cook emerged from the kitchen. "She could stay home with me. We could have a girls' weekend," she said, smiling warmly at Ellen.

"You're sure you don't want to go?" the king asked.

"Sure," Ellen said resolutely.

"But you're still coming, dear?" he asked the queen.

"Yes. I love *Star Journey* movies. I like the idea of a girls' weekend, too, but I'll go to the festival."

"It's settled then," the king said. "The only other thing I need to know is what's for dessert," he said, grinning at Cook.

That weekend, the royal family, **sans** Ellen, hurried to the Film Festival's entrance in Verb Village. The queen was stressed because she'd had trouble finding their tickets.

★ ★ ★ ★ ★ ★ ★ ★ ★

sans – *without*

★ ★ ★ ★ ★ ★ ★ ★ ★

She was further aggravated by the king's suggestion on how to avoid being disorganized in the future.

When they were admitted, the king was astonished by the crowd. "There are so many here. It's going to be a nightmare getting around," he said.

The queen sighed in exasperation. "It's fine! We have reserved seats. Let's make our way to Theater A. That's where the *Star Journey* movie is showing."

The four of them struggled to make their way through the crowd of words. Once they found and took their seats in the theater, Luke looked around at the rest of the audience members. "There seem to be a lot of word pairs here," he noted.

"Word pairs?" the king repeated, still grumpy about the mass of attendees.

"Every pair seems to include the word *to*," Kirk noted. "*To do, to watch, to go.*"

The king looked around the theater and sighed. "Infinitives," he grumbled.

"What's the problem?" the queen asked. "They love these movies like we do. I don't see any harm in it."

The king decided not to make an issue of it. He could tell his wife was already agitated by his negativity. He put on a phony smile and said he was sure the movie would be great.

After the film was over, the royal family had to be aggressive to get past the words who took their time leaving the theater. "Getting out was a challenge, but what did you think of the movie?" the queen asked once they were outside.

"It was fun! I enjoyed it," the king said. "Wish I could say the same for this crowd."

The two boys agreed that the movie was one of the better films in the *Star Journey* series. But their attention was quickly drawn to the crowd of words moving past them.

"So many verbs," Luke noted. "*Talking, watched, bought.* They're all here."

"This is Verb Village. That makes sense," the queen said. The queen's communicator vibrated. When she glanced at it, she saw that it was Ellen. "Everything okay?" she asked her.

"Yes," Ellen said unconvincingly.

"What's wrong?"

"Nothing serious. But we are having trouble talk."

The queen covered her ear so she could hear Ellen better. "You're having trouble talking?"

"Yes, talk. I wanted watch a movie with Cook, only I couldn't say it," Ellen explained.

"I understand you, though," the queen said, hoping to dismiss the problem quickly.

"We can understand each other. But it's like words are miss."

"Missing? You mean missing? Like what words?"

"Uh, words like cook, play, read," Ellen said. "But that's not what I mean."

"Ellen, it's really noisy here. Will you be okay until we get home from the festival?"

"Yes," Ellen said, sighing in disappointment.

"Okay. Have a good time! We will tell you all about the festival when we get back," the queen said, ending the call.

"What was all that about?" the king said as he kept being shoved by words trying to get past him.

"Oh, she said there are some words missing. I think she just regrets staying home," the queen explained.

"What words?"

"That's just it. She said them with no problem. She said *cook, play, read.*"

The king stood and watched as words streamed past them.

"What is it, dear?" the queen asked.

"Participles and infinitives," he said. "That's all I see. Why? I'm going to find out." Without explaining, he started walking to the front gate of the festival. The queen and the boys followed him so they wouldn't get separated.

When they arrived at the entrance, the king approached a ticket taker. "What are your ticket prices for words?" he asked.

"Participles and infinitives get in free. Seats aren't reserved. It's $500 a word for the rest." he said robotically.

"Why the difference?" the king asked.

"Mister, I just work here," he said dismissively.

The king reddened at the lack of respect. He withdrew from the front gate and told his family, "There are so many participles and infinitives here that they are unavailable for use on planet English."

"What are you going to do?" Kirk asked him.

"Forcing these verbs out of the festival isn't an option. They will revolt." He was silent for a moment, thinking. "But we could ask them for their tickets as they go into the theaters. They don't have reserved seats. They only have admission to the festival. When they aren't allowed to see the films, they'll get bored and go home," the king explained.

"I'm afraid I'll let some participles and infinitives in by mistake. It's been a while since we did those missions," Luke said.

"I could ask Ellen to consult the guidebook and send out a mission. Then the guardians can send us a list of participles and infinitives that shouldn't be allowed into the theater. I think Ellen will be happy that she was right," the queen said, smiling.

"Contact her right away," the king urged.

110

What does *dispassionate* mean?

What part of speech is the word pair *to be*?

Why was Ellen able to say *cook, play,* and *read*?

Chapter 24

The king, queen, and their two boys were about to board a shuttle to return to planet English. They were exhausted after working as ticket takers at the Film Festival. That's when the king's communicator buzzed. It was the Prime Minister.

"Your Highness, where are you?" the Prime Minister asked. The king explained that they were about to travel home from planet Sentence. "Stay there. We have a crisis," he said breathlessly.

"What sort of crisis?"

"Dependent clauses have declared their independence from your rule. Phrases are joining them in **seceding**."

"They can't do that."

"I know that, you know that, but they don't seem to know that," the Prime Minister said. "And the media is **championing** their cause."

★ ★ ★ ★ ★ ★ ★ ★ ★ ★

seceding – *separating*

championing – *supporting*

★ ★ ★ ★ ★ ★ ★ ★ ★ ★

"Of course they are," the king said, sighing. "All right. We will stay until we can get this sorted out."

"Let me know what I can do to help," the Prime Minister said.

"We're not going home," the queen concluded without trying to hide her disappointment.

"Unfortunately, no. The Gremlin has clauses convinced that they should be independent. I have to do whatever it takes to quash that notion," he said gravely.

When the four of them arrived at Clause Center and exited the space tram, they were astonished by the size of the crowd.

Phrases and clauses surrounded a platform on which a speaker addressed them. "'Independence is loyalty to one's best self and principles,' Mark Twain said. It's time for every clause to be loyal to its best self, rather than to a dictator who thinks he knows what is best," she said smugly. The crowd noisily approved.

The king reddened and began approaching the platform.

"Dear, count to three," the queen advised.

"One, two, three," the king said angrily, as he strode to the platform. He climbed the steps and approached the speaker. "I'm sure you'll allow me time to respond," he said icily.

"Certainly," the speaker said, **ostentatiously** stepping back from the microphone.

★ ★ ★ ★ ★ ★ ★ ★ ★

ostentatiously – *showily*

★ ★ ★ ★ ★ ★ ★ ★ ★

Before he could speak, reporters shouted out questions. "Do you think it's right that only some clauses have independence? How can you justify forced dependence in a free galaxy? Why don't clauses have a say in their governing?"

"Listen," the king said, interrupting them. "I first want to say that clauses are heroes in this galaxy. We depend on you in our writing and speaking. And before I'm criticized for not mentioning them, the phrases that are here are heroes, too." The king could tell by the quiet that he was getting through to them.

"You are heroes because in the words of Bob Dylan, 'A hero is someone who understands the responsibility that comes with his freedom.' You have freedom to come here and protest. And you also have responsibilities—important ones to your planet and your galaxy. Without clauses that remain dependent, the clause 'After the rally' would be a complete sentence. That makes no sense. Adjective clauses like 'that started at noon' would be complete sentences, too. I can't emphasize enough the confusion and chaos that would result.

"So, after the rally, what will you do? To use some of you adverbial phrases out there, while you are on the way home, as you gather with other clauses, and before you go to bed. These phrases need independent clauses (with a subject, verb, and a complete thought) to make meaningful sentences.

"I know this is a big decision. So here is what I'm going to do. I will have our grammar guardians show you why we need some clauses and phrases to remain a dependent part of sentences. Are you willing to hear from them before you decide on independence?"

The king's question was met with silence at first but then with reluctant agreement. "You won't be sorry!" he said enthusiastically. "And thank you for everything you do," he said, applauding them.

Reporters circled the king, peppering him with questions as he left the platform. "I have important work to do," he replied, brushing them off.

He found the queen and the two boys, who expressed their enthusiasm for his speech. "Thank you for your support," he said, putting his hands on their shoulders. "Now we have to ask Ellen to send another mission, ironically enough, independently."

The queen contacted her and explained their predicament. She was relieved when Ellen seemed happy to send out a mission on clauses and phrases.

What does *ostentatiously* mean?

What is an independent clause?

Why shouldn't all clauses be independent?

Chapter 25

Everyone in the royal family was happy that the clauses and phrases had agreed not to secede. The king was even more thrilled when he learned that planet Sentence was planning a parade to celebrate. But he declined to speak when the parade organizer invited him to.

"I am honored by the invitation, but I am just home from a two-week trip to the planet. I have a lot of work to get caught up on. I hope you understand," the king had said.

The organizer was gracious and wished the king well. "I hope you'll be able to watch the parade. It will be streamed around the galaxy," she said.

"I wouldn't miss it," he promised.

The following weekend, the royal family and Cook gathered in the media room to watch the parade.

First up was a marching band. The queen said she wondered if she would have enjoyed being in band.

"With your cold intolerance, I would say no," the king joked.

"You're probably right," the queen said, laughing at herself.

Next in the parade were some giant balloons, some jugglers, and some clowns.

Sentences walked by next. Luke read one out loud. "Always coming to the rescue...the Gremlin..."

"What?" the king said, raising his voice. "The Gremlin isn't always coming to the rescue."

"Let him finish, dear," the queen urged.

"Was no match...for our king," Luke read.

"You see? The Gremlin was no match for you. You got upset for nothing," the queen said. "Oh, look! Another sentence is coming."

"The king...left the Gremlin...on the planet...he defeated," Luke read.

"They're saying I defeated the planet...not the Gremlin," the king complained.

Luke continued, ignoring his father's reaction. "Looking around the planet...chaos is everywhere."

"That's a dangling participle!" the king cried.

"No one likes to be criticized, but did you leave the planet in chaos? Is it true?" the queen asked solemnly.

"What? No! You were with me. I stopped the ridiculous quest for independence by dependent clauses. That's what I did," the king said, defending himself.

"The parade organizer...said the tight king's schedule...kept him from speaking today," Luke read.

"They did that on purpose," the king said, pointing to the screen. "The **gall** of that parade organizer! Tight king," he muttered.

★ ★ ★ ★ ★ ★ ★ ★ ★

gall – *nerve*

★ ★ ★ ★ ★ ★ ★ ★ ★

"Well, you are 'thrifty,'" the queen said, using air quotes.

The king shook his hands in frustration. "Don't you see what's happening here?"

"You're becoming **irascible**?" the queen answered hesitantly.

★ ★ ★ ★ ★ ★ ★ ★ ★ ★

irascible – *irritable*

farce – *embarrassment*

★ ★ ★ ★ ★ ★ ★ ★ ★ ★

"Ugh! These are misplaced modifiers. The whole parade is a **farce**. The Gremlin has the sentence parts walking the parade out of order to humiliate me," the king exclaimed, his face turning scarlet.

"Dear, calm down. Mel Wright says no one has the power to humilate us without our permission," the queen said sanctimoniously.

"Is that so? Mel Wright, the Gremlin fan girl. Now you're a fan girl, too? I'm seeing what you're up to slowly," the king replied, eyes narrowed.

Cook interjected to reduce the tension. "I have some apple pie in the kitchen for Your hot Majesty." Cook's face reddened when she realized what she'd said.

The king and queen looked at her in astonishment and then laughed.

"Now you understand, don't you?" the king asked the queen.

"Yes. The words are being mixed up in the parade and it's mixing us up, too," the queen said. "I'm sorry, dear," she said, rising to hug him. "I'm your girl fan forever."

The king laughed again. "I know what you mean," he told the queen, hugging her back. "Thinking about it, the apple pie will help us all," he said to Cook. "Ack! I can't stop using misplaced modifiers."

"What are misplaced modifiers again?" Luke asked.

"They're words, phrases, or clauses that are separated from the word they explain, resulting in an uncertain meaning," the king said.

"The parade is still going," Kirk said, pointing to the screen.

As the camera zoomed out on the parade route, Ellen said, "And look how many sentences are still in line!"

The king groaned. "Okay. We can have pie, but then we will need to return to planet Sentence. We'll have to take the spaceporter this time."

"Are you thinking we need to send a review mission on misplaced modifiers?" Kirk asked.

"Precisely," the king answered. "We'll need the guardians' help getting the sentences in the correct order before they walk the parade route."

What does *gall* mean?

What is a misplaced modifier?

What did Cook mean to say?

Chapter 26

"Have you heard about the new documentary coming out this week?" the queen asked the king at breakfast.

"No. Who's it about?" he asked, eating a forkful of egg.

"Not who, what. It's about punctuation. It's called *Punctuation Appropriation*."

"Appropriation? What on English?" the king said, laughing. "The media **oligarchs** are saying that our punctuation marks are unethical? That's laughable."

★ ★ ★ ★ ★ ★ ★ ★ ★

appropriation – *stealing*

oligarchs – *dictators*

supplanted – *replaced*

★ ★ ★ ★ ★ ★ ★ ★ ★

"The trailer says that it's based on extensive historical research. 'The researchers' conclusion will shock the galaxy,'" the queen repeated.

"Yes, I'm sure it's utterly scandalous," the king said mockingly.

"I plan to watch it anyway," the queen said, raising her chin in defiance.

"Good. You can give me the funny highlights," the king said, smirking. He returned his attention to his breakfast.

On an evening the following week, the king and queen were sitting in the media room. The queen was scrolling through home decorating ideas on her tablet while the king watched the news.

"Parliament is considering taking action after a new documentary revealed the truth about punctuation in the galaxy," the broadcaster said. "Evidence that periods and commas were the original punctuation marks that were **supplanted** by colons and semicolons has created controversy."

"What?" the king said aloud.

"The Original Punctuation Bill would prohibit other marks from being used if periods and commas fit the sentence. To preserve the galaxy's history, the bill's sponsor hopes colons and semicolons can be phased out," the broadcaster continued.

Video of the sponsor filled the screen. "It's the right thing to do, and less punctuation marks will make life simpler for all of us."

"Fewer!" the king retorted. "And fewer punctuation marks will not make life simpler. This is preposterous."

He turned his attention to the queen, who was still scrolling on her tablet. "You said you would tell me what was in this documentary," he said accusingly.

"No. You said to tell you the funny parts, and there were no funny parts," she said, continuing to focus on her tablet.

The king sighed. "I was wrong to assume the documentary was meaningless. I'm sorry."

"Thank you," the queen said matter of factly.

"Do you truly forgive me?"

It was the queen's turn to sigh. "Yes. I was probably being too sensitive about it. But don't you dare accuse me of being too sensitive the next time we disagree," she teased him.

"King's honor," he said, saluting her. "Will you tell me what I need to know about this documentary?" he asked.

"It said that periods and commas were the only punctuation marks at first. Then colons and semicolons came and took some of their responsibilities away."

"What proof did they present for this?"

"Let me think. They showed some old books."

"Those old books didn't have colons or semicolons?" the king pressed.

"Hm. I don't know. They didn't zoom in. I just remember periods and commas seeming to be depressed while sad music played."

"You know that punctuation marks don't get depressed, right?" the king nodded to get his wife's agreement.

"Yes," she said uncertainly at first, "yes, I know. I just don't want anyone to feel left out."

"Of course you don't because you are a caring person," he said, covering her hand with his. "Thank you for filling me in. I have some research to do now," he said.

"You're preparing to debate them, aren't you?" the queen said, smiling.

The king just laughed as he left for the castle library.

In the library, the king found a reference on the history of grammar. As he scanned the table of contents, he chided himself for not doing more history reading. When he found an article on the history of punctuation, he read it carefully.

After reading several paragraphs, he knew he had what he needed to defend the colon and semicolon. He'd learned that the comma was actually a later addition to punctuation. Even the period hadn't been originally intended to end a sentence. Instead, the placement of a dot in a string of words meant a short, medium, or long pause.

The king pondered the role of punctuation in the galaxy. He wasn't surprised that a documentary like *Punctuation Appropriation* had misled people. History was important, yes. But what the galaxy truly needed was a reminder of the purpose of punctuation. Colons were used to give more information and semicolons were used to show a pause longer than a comma but shorter than a period. Semicolons were particularly needed to list items that contained commas.

His first task was to have the children send out a mission on punctuation. But he also had a big idea. He would produce a documentary called *Punctuation Purpose.* He hoped it would get Parliament to drop the Original Punctuation Bill.

What does *appropriation* mean?

When are semicolons particularly important?

How did the *Punctuation Appropriation* documentary try to change opinions?

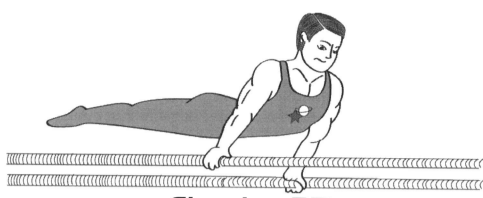

Chapter 27

The royal family and Cook gathered in the media room to watch the Olympic Games. Cook had decorated cookies just for the occasion.

On this particular evening, gymnastics events were on the schedule. "Gymnastics is my favorite event to watch," Ellen gushed.

"Mine too," Cook agreed.

"Looks like it's men's parallel bars and women's floor competitions tonight," Kirk said.

Ellen clapped in enthusiasm. "I can't wait!"

An announcer gave an overview of the parallel bars competition. "We have several contenders for gold tonight. We don't know who is the favorite because of the cancellation of this event after the Galaxy Championships."

"What a terrible night that was," a co-announcer added. "To see an athlete take a fall like that...It could have ended his career." While he spoke, a replay of the gymnast rotating forward, slipping through the bars, and hitting the mat face-first filled the screen.

Even though Ellen and the queen had witnessed the accident in person, they gasped.

"But we're happy to tell you that he not only recovered but is with us competing tonight," the first announcer said, beaming.

"That's right! You'd have to think the accident is on his mind, though," the co-announcer said.

"We know that everyone here is wishing him luck," the announcer said, gesturing to the crowd behind him. "The competition is starting, so let's watch."

The first competitor did his routine with a clean landing, earning a respectable score. "The judges are leaving room for an extraordinary performance later in the competition, I think," the co-announcer said.

A second competitor completed his routine with a stabilizing step on the landing. He seemed disappointed in his score that had him in second place.

"Next up is the young man who took the fall at the Championships. This is a **pivotal** moment for him," the announcer said dramatically.

★ ★ ★ ★ ★ ★ ★ ★ ★ ★

pivotal – decisive

impeccable – flawless

conferring – discussing

★ ★ ★ ★ ★ ★ ★ ★ ★ ★

The gymnast chalked his hands and stared at the mat, mentally affirming his ability to perform an **impeccable** routine.

He mounted the bars and extended into a handstand. After swinging backward, he performed a half twist.

"Looks solid," the co-announcer observed.

But as the gymnast did a forward flip, he rotated too far forward and slipped through the bars, hitting the mat with a loud thwack.

The announcers and audience gasped in horror. *Not again!* they thought. How could he possibly survive another fall?

His trainer ran over to him, but by the time he got to him, the gymnast was on his feet. The gymnast waved to the crowd as if to say he was fine. This gesture was met with relief and enthusiastic applause.

"Whew! I'm so glad he is okay," the announcer said, speaking for the spectators as well. "I see the judges are **conferring**. Are they going to give him another chance?"

"That would be highly unusual for the Olympic Games," the co-announcer said. "Wait! It looks like a judge is going to make an announcement."

The judge cleared her throat and addressed the competitors and crowd. "In light of a second life-threatening fall on the parallel bars, we are suspending this event. Athletes' safety is our top priority." She sat down amidst widespread murmuring.

"What about the competitors who have already done this event? It seems so unfair!" Ellen cried.

"It does," the king agreed. "The gymnast was okay. Canceling the event seems like a major overreaction."

"You might not feel the same way if it were Kirk out there competing," the queen said.

The king frowned and ignored the personal example. "These competitors know the risks. Believe me, they've fallen many times."

The queen shrugged. "Well, it's not our decision."

They dropped the discussion and watched the women's floor routine.

The next day, Cook asked the king if he wanted something special for breakfast. "Hm. I think I would like eggs, bacon, and to have some fresh fruit." Then he frowned.

"Are you not sure about that?" Cook asked.

"No, I mean yes. I'm sure, but it came out wrong."

"It's early," Cook joked.

"It is," he said, smiling at her.

He picked up the newspaper and read the front-page story about the parallel-bars event being canceled. "A handstand, a twist, then the gymnast fell on a flip forward. His commitment to train, to persevere, and compete were on display last night. But the judges' concern for safety overruled the competitors' and spectators'."

"Not this again," the king groaned. He continued to read.

"Out of an abundance of caution, authorities on planet Sentence have suspended parallel structure."

"You don't say," the king said sarcastically.

When the children came for breakfast, he explained what was happening. Although safety in a gymnastics event had nothing to do with sentences, the Gremlin had used it as an opportunity to cause chaos.

"What's parallel structure again?" Ellen asked.

"It means using the same grammatical composition in a sentence. The lack of parallelism is most apparent in lists. This morning I told Cook I wanted bacon, eggs, and to have some fresh fruit. I used two nouns and an infinitive in the list," the king said.

"And you should have said you wanted bacon, eggs, and to have some fresh fruit," Luke said, scrunching his face up in frustration. "That's not what I meant to say."

"We need to send out a review mission, don't we?" Kirk asked.

"Yes, and we'll also need to have the guardians write letters to the authorities, asking for the suspension to be lifted," the king said. "My hope is that they will cave in to the pressure."

The three children finished their breakfast and began work on a Parallel Structure mission.

What does *pivotal* mean?

What is parallel structure?

What should the king have said he wanted for breakfast, using parallel structure?

Unit V: Adventures in Composition & Speaking

Chapter 28

"I can't wait until the new *Spaceman* book comes out!" Luke gushed on their walk to the main library branch.

"When is it supposed to be published?" the king asked.

"A new one comes out around this time every year."

"You'll have to request it as soon as the library gets a copy," the king said. "Let's ask the librarian if they have a date for it."

"Great idea!" Luke said, walking ahead of the family at a fast pace.

The king laughed at his enthusiasm. "I appreciate your love for reading, Luke."

"Who doesn't like reading?" Luke said as though the idea were preposterous.

When they reached the library, Luke got the attention of the head librarian. "Do you know when the next *Spaceman* book will be out?" he asked her.

"Uh, no," she said hesitantly. "I don't. Uh. Hm. Have you read the *Star Journey* books, based on the movies?

"All of them," Luke said. "You have no clue when the *Spaceman* book will be out? You're not just trying to keep it a secret?"

The librarian looked alarmed when she heard the word secret. "No, no, why would you say that? I promise to let you know the moment we receive it," she said, looking anxiously at the king.

"He's just a little excited," the king said apologetically.

"I understand. A lot of people are," the librarian said, smiling.

But the king wasn't fooled by her smile. He noted her furrowed brow as she checked her computer screen.

Luke sighed. "I'll have to find something else to read while I wait."

"Yes. Try a new genre! It'll make the time pass," the king suggested.

As Luke left to browse the shelves, a girl approached the circulation desk and called the librarian over. "Do you know when the new *Last Kids in the Galaxy* book will be available?" she asked.

"Uh, hm. I'm not sure," the libarian stammered. "I haven't been notified of a publication date. Do you get our weekly newsletter? I put popular new releases in there."

The girl hung her head in disappointment. She said she wasn't sure if they got the newsletter but would ask her parents.

The king frowned at this interaction. He kept thinking about it as he looked for books to check out.

On the walk back home, the king mentioned his concerns to his wife. "Why would the librarian be so nervous when asked about title release dates?"

"Maybe because she knows how upset some kids get. And she definitely doesn't want to upset you of all people."

"I suppose. Just seemed strange," he mused.

The next week, Luke hadn't been contacted by the librarian and complained. "We shouldn't expect the book to be available right away. I'm sorry," the king said. Maybe kids' disappointment was the reason the librarian was acting strangely, he thought.

He went to find the queen to tell her she was correct. He found her in her study, staring at her computer screen. "Hello! I'm here to tell you that you were right. It's the second time or so," he joked. He explained that Luke was already pestering him about the *Spaceman* book. Clearly the main librarian had to cope with this all the time.

"Yes," the queen said numbly. "I thought so."

"Hey!" the king said, ignoring her **apathy**. "I haven't asked you how your new mystery is coming along. But you normally tell me about your plot twists. Are you keeping it a secret?"

★ ★ ★ ★ ★ ★ ★ ★ ★ ★

apathy – *indifference*

woodenly – *unconvincingly*

★ ★ ★ ★ ★ ★ ★ ★ ★ ★

"Yes, I mean no. Uh, it takes time to write a novel," she said **woodenly**.

"I know it does. But you've been working on it for quite a while. Why don't you give me a hint?" he said, trying to peek at her screen.

"Don't!" she said, blocking the screen with her hands.

The king recoiled in surprise. "If you feel so strongly about keeping it secret, don't worry. I won't ask," he said, his hurt turning to anger.

"Okay, thank you," the queen retorted. She collapsed onto her keyboard when her husband left in a huff.

The next day, the king received his copy of *Galaxy Book List* magazine. He always looked forward to reading it, though he was often overwhelmed by the **plethora** of options. He hadn't even read the front cover before picking up the magazine. But as he sat in

★ ★ ★ ★ ★ ★ ★ ★ ★ ★

plethora – *overabundance*

★ ★ ★ ★ ★ ★ ★ ★ ★ ★

the sunroom to read it, he took in the headline: Has Writer's Block Hit the Galaxy?

He squeezed his eyes shut, hoping the headline would disappear. But there it was when he looked again. He hoped it was hyperbole and began reading the article.

"Many of the galaxy's top authors have missed their publication deadlines, according to publishers we contacted. Fans of popular series are left waiting with no word on when to expect the next title. We also spoke to the galaxy's head librarian and asked for her comment. She said she is usually given advance notice of the release dates for series titles. But publishers aren't giving her the information now."

"She knows," the king said aloud. "She knows it's Writer's Block and she doesn't want to cause panic." Then the king gasped. "My wife has it. There was nothing on her screen. She hasn't been writing. What do I do? I'm a grammar expert, not a psychologist." He decided to break the news to the kids.

"We've been through this before," Kirk said calmly after hearing the news.

"Yes, but I think this outbreak is much worse," the king said.

"What did we do before?" Ellen asked. "Let's look it up in the guidebook." Ellen led the way to the castle library where she found *The Guide to Grammar* Galaxy and the article about Writer's Block within it. She read aloud for the group.

Writer's Block
Writer's block is difficulty knowing what to write. Often it occurs because the

writer wants the work to be perfect. Or, the writer fears having the writing judged. Writer's block can be worse when there is time pressure.

To cure writer's block (or be immune to it), write without judging the work. Don't think about what other people will think of your writing. Write anything, even if it isn't related to the project. For example, write about writer's block. Then work on your project again. Or instead of writing, work on the outline or plan for the project. You can try reading for inspiration. Also, be sure to start early on a writing project and work consistently.

"This is good," Ellen said. "But I remember another mission we did that could help. It was coming up with new ideas for writing."

"Possibility thinking?" Kirk asked.

"That's it!" Ellen turned to the article on possibility thinking in the guidebook and read it aloud.

Possibility Thinking

Possibility thinking in creative writing is brainstorming or generating many ideas without criticism. The more ideas a writer thinks about, the more creative the ideas are likely to be. For example, instead of coming up with three space story ideas, come up with 30.

Ask yourself the following questions using the acronym SCAMPER* to create more possibilities:

What if I **substituted** something? (the ocean for space)

What if I **combined** something? (ninjas in space)

What if I **adapted** (changed) something? (a spacecraft that can also go underground)

What if I **magnified** something? (added another universe)

What if I **put** something to another use? (a robot that can also be flown)

What if I **eliminated** something? (spacecraft that battle without pilots)

What if I **rearranged** or **reversed** something? (the people think the hero is evil)

These questions can be used over and over again to create story ideas.

The SCAMPER acronym is based on the work of Alex Osborn and Bob Eberle.

The king opened the door to the library.

"Where are you going?" Luke asked.

"To call someone about producing a public service announcement. We'll stress the importance of creative writing exercises to keep the galaxy healthy."

"You mean you won't say Writer's Block?" Kirk asked.

"Precisely. I also need you three to send out a mission called Creative Exercises. I'll suggest to your mother that doing them together would be fun." He winked and left.

What does *plethora* mean?

What is possibility thinking?

Why didn't the king want to mention writer's block to the media?

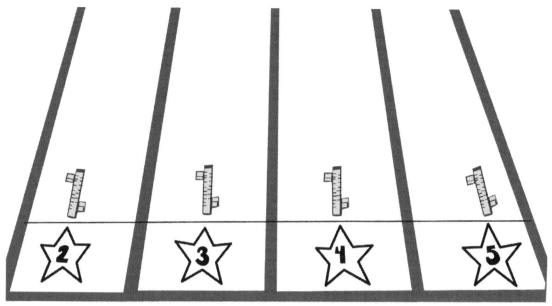

Chapter 29

"Is your robotics team ready to compete this weekend?" the king asked Kirk at dinner.

"The team is as ready as it can be," Kirk said, smiling confidently.

"What's your strategy?" the king asked.

"The strategy is **iterative** improvement. The way to win is with **commensurate** funding. The team will focus on working hard and being organized. The new approach is to take shortcuts when it makes sense."

★ ★ ★ ★ ★ ★ ★ ★ ★ ★

iterative – *continual*

commensurate – *equal*

★ ★ ★ ★ ★ ★ ★ ★ ★ ★

"Shortcuts? I thought that was a bad idea," the king said.

"The use of shortcuts can be smart. The example I can give you is to purchase a quality gearbox rather than building one."

"Oh, I see," the king said rubbing his beard.

"The focus is on making everything faster," Kirk added.

"I don't even know what a gearbox is," Ellen joked.

"The gearbox determines the speed and direction of the robot arms," Kirk said.

"Oh," Ellen replied.

"The motor supplies the energy."

132

Ellen nodded politely. "We should play our new board game tonight," she said to change the topic of conversation.

"The board game looks interesting," Kirk said.

Ellen arched an eyebrow. Kirk was acting strangely, she thought.

"The concept is intriguing. The object of the game is to argue that your character would overcome another in a battle," Kirk continued.

"That's right. In other words, it should be fun," Ellen joked.

"I'm looking forward to it," the king said.

That evening, the family met in the game room to play.

"The game is actually a card game, not a board game. The object of the game is to convince the judge that your characters would win the battle. The game is about being a good debater," Kirk said.

"You should all be good at it then," the king teased.

"The best preparation for playing the game is to review principles of debate," Kirk said.

"That may be, but we're not going to do that now. We're going to play the game," Ellen said tersely.

"The debate format that most applies to the game is Lincoln Douglas. The first speaker makes a case for or against a resolution. The resolution is a policy statement that they are discussing. The second speaker asks questions about the first speech in cross-examination," Kirk said.

Ellen erupted. "We're not talking about debate, Kirk! We're playing a game for galaxy's sake."

"Ellen!" the queen said to chastise her for her outburst.

"I'm sorry, but Kirk is being so **domineering**, and it's my game," Ellen said, crossing her arms in in a pout.

★ ★ ★ ★ ★ ★ ★ ★ ★ ★

domineering – *bossy*

★ ★ ★ ★ ★ ★ ★ ★ ★ ★

"The truth is I am not being domineering; I'm educating you," Kirk said calmly.

"We're not your robotics team, Kirk," Ellen said, still angry.

"The fact that you are not my robotics team is apparent," Kirk said woodenly.

"It does seem like you have been spending too much time working on robotics. You sound like a robot," Luke joked.

"Luke!" the queen objected. But she had to admit to herself that he had a point. "The solution is to just play the game," she said.

"The idea your mother has is mine, too," the king said, puzzled at his words.

"The game won't get played by just talking about it," Luke agreed.

"The fun seems to be gone now," Ellen said, crestfallen.

"The right attitude can make all the difference," the queen said, disagreeing.

"The hour is not late," Kirk added, agreeing.

"The problem is how you're talking, Kirk," Luke said.

"The way you're talking, too," the king told Luke.

"The way I'm talking!" he added, alarmed by his words. "The problem must not be Kirk's robotics team."

The king got up and tapped the screen to activate it. "Your Majesty?" Screen responded.

"The status of planet Sentence, please," the king said.

"The Sentence Relays are in progress, Your Highness."

"The relay races? The video feed, please," the king requested.

Video of sentences running relay races on a track filled the screen.

Ellen said what they were all thinking. "The word *the* is the starter for every sentence again!"

"The starting word has to vary or sentences get repetitive and robotic," the king said. "The solution is to use a variety of sentence starters."

"The problem is I don't remember the other sentence starters," Luke said.

The king responded by motioning for the family to follow him to the castle library. He read the article on sentence starters in *The Guide to Grammar Galaxy* aloud.

Sentence Starters

There are a number of ways to begin a sentence to keep your readers' interest. Rather than beginning with an article adjective (a, an, the) or the subject of the sentence, try beginning your sentence with:

- **an adverb** *Slowly* the man backed away from the bear.
- **a prepositional phrase** *At the start of the game*, the kids got along well.
- **a participle** *Gasping* for breath, the swimmer emerged from the water.

- **two adjectives** *Cold and hungry*, the skier entered the warm cabin.
- **transition words** *Third*, let the paint dry for eight hours.
- **subordinating conjunctions** *Whether* it rains or not, we are having the picnic.

These sentence starters will keep your writing from sounding repetitive.

"The next thing you'll say is that we need to go to planet Sentence and switch up these sentence starters," Luke told his father.

"The task that needs to be done first is writing a mission on sentence starters," Kirk said.

Ellen was disappointed about delaying the game but agreed to help write the mission.

What does *iterative* mean?

Why should sentence starters vary?

Why did Luke think Kirk sounded like a robot?

Chapter 30

It was Saturday afternoon and the king was eager to do something active. The king hadn't overindulged at breakfast, so he had plenty of energy. He wanted his family to join him.

He asked his wife first. "Would you like to work out with me?"

"Not today," she answered absentmindedly, looking at her tablet.

The king was disappointed. "It's been a while since you've worked out though, right?" he asked **pointedly**.

The queen breathed out slowly to calm herself. "I was just being educated about **assertiveness**. The formula for it is by Dr. Yielding. Here goes! *I feel* angry *when you* imply that I'm lazy *and I need* you to accept my answer without criticizing me."

★ ★ ★ ★ ★ ★ ★ ★ ★ ★

pointedly – *sharply*

assertiveness – *firmness*

obstinate – *stubborn*

★ ★ ★ ★ ★ ★ ★ ★ ★ ★

"Does that mean you're not going to work out with me? Yes or no?" the king asked.

"No!" the queen said too loudly. She started searching Dr. Yielding's article for help with **obstinate** people like her husband.

"Okay then," the king said, muttering to himself as he left the room. "I'll get the boys to work out with me."

The king found Kirk and Luke in the game room with virtual headsets on. "Hey! How about some real fun? Let's work out," the king said as a command rather than a suggestion.

The boys didn't respond at first as they interacted with the virtual game world they were seeing.

"Hey! Can you hear me?" the king asked loudly.

"Yes! Sorry, Father," Luke said. "The game had me really focused."

"I see that," the king said, frowning in disapproval. "I asked if you wanted to work out with me."

"Uh," Luke said, staring at the floor.

"We've been asked by some top players to join their team," Kirk said apologetically.

"You're saying you don't want to work out," the king groaned.

Luke nodded sheepishly.

"When are you going to exercise then? You know how important it is."

"Later. The promise is made," Luke said, putting his headset back on.

The king considered delaying his workout so they could join him. But he was eager to start and wanted company. He decided to ask Ellen.

Ellen was in her room on her communicator when her father called her name. "Just a minute, Cher. I'm being summoned by my father," she said. She put the communicator down and opened her door.

"I'm going to work out. Why don't you join me for a father-daughter date?" the king asked warmly.

"Oh, that would be fun. But I'm needed by Cher right now." She added in a whisper, "Girl stuff."

"Uh-huh," the king said without trying to hide his disappointment. As he left Ellen's room, he was deflated. He thought about the negative response he had gotten from his family when the truth hit him: His family didn't care about fitness. He had failed in this area. No, *they* had failed in this area.

He began to walk more quickly as he prepared to talk with the queen. She had to join him in insisting that everyone work out.

The queen was still reading on her tablet when the king burst into the room. "No one wants to work out with me. We've failed. This family doesn't value physical fitness. You have to set a good example by working out with me and insisting that the kids join us," he said breathlessly.

The queen's mouth fell open in shock. "Dr. Yielding, help!" she said to herself as she stared at her tablet. "The assertiveness formula was used. Now what?"

"More like passive formula! You are being lied to. You are being used. You are..." the king stopped in the middle of his rant. "Passive," he said with sudden understanding. "I have been duped by the Gremlin once again." His shoulders drooped in defeat. "I'm sorry, dear."

The king got Screen's attention and asked for a status update on planet Sentence. A video appeared on the screen with a woman addressing a crowd. "The best way to ensure peace in the galaxy is to make passive voices louder than active ones."

"Dr. Yielding!" the queen exclaimed, pointing at the screen.

"Why am I being surprised?" the king asked. "Once again we have passive voice dominating us. The children have to be told," he said. He reached for the queen's hand. "My ways have to be changed," he admitted. "I hope to be forgiven by you."

The queen nodded and stood to hug him.

The king had Kirk, Luke, and Ellen meet him in the castle library. There he explained the situation and read them the article on passive voice from *The Guide to Grammar Galaxy*.

Passive Voice

Passive voice is when the subject of a sentence is being acted upon. A sentence is in passive voice when a form of *be* (is, am, are, was, were, being, been) is paired with the past participle of the verb (i.e., the present or past perfect verb often ending in -ed).

The passive agent (that acts on the subject) may be added to the sentence with the word *by*.

Most telescopes **are manufactured** in China and Taiwan.
A new space program will **be launched** in two years.
Pluto **was discovered by Clyde Tombaugh**. (passive agent)

Verbs that cannot have direct objects are never in passive voice (e.g., arrive, come, die, go, live, sleep).

Active voice emphasizes the subject as the acting agent.

China and Taiwan **manufacture** the most telescopes.
The country **will launch** a new space program in two years.
Clyde Tombaugh **discovered** Pluto.

Use passive voice sparingly. Active voice makes sentences easier to understand.

"A mission on passive voice has to be sent. Dr. Yielding has to be stopped. Does a workout also have to be completed?" Luke asked.

"That is something that will have to be discussed," the king said, smiling.

What does *pointedly* mean in the story?

What is a verb that is never in passive voice?

How would "My ways have to be changed" be written in active voice?

Chapter 31

The head programmer came to the king's study. "We need to talk," he said with a sense of urgency.

The king welcomed him without hesitation. He surmised that something was wrong. Or perhaps he wanted a raise?

"What is it?" he asked the programmer, inviting him to be seated.

"We are nearing storage capacity on planet Composition," he said breathlessly.

"You mean we are running out of room for books? Are you serious?"

"Yes, I'm serious. I spoke with the head librarian there and she said they are running out of space for print books. My concern is that we have limited storage for digital books and articles as well. The rare galaxy minerals used to make digital storage devices are in low supply."

"To solve the first problem, we can just build more bookshelves. That's what we've always done," the king said.

"We *are* building more bookshelves, but we need places to put them. The Library of the Galaxy is having to make the aisles narrower to accommodate more shelves while they add on to the building."

"I don't think you can ever have too many bookshelves, even if you have to expand the space. But what about these rare minerals?" the king asked.

"Yes. There are 17 metals in the soil that are used to create electronic devices like communicators and the computers that form the internet. These devices store digital versions of books and articles. The metals used to create them aren't truly rare; they're everywhere in the galaxy. But we don't have enough companies mining and refining them for use in production. It's a time-consuming process. And we're quickly running out of digital storage space."

"I see," the king said, stroking his beard. "So you think I should increase the pace of construction to house our print books. And you also want me to **coax** more companies to mine rare minerals?" the king asked.

★ ★ ★ ★ ★ ★ ★ ★ ★ ★

coax – *persuade*

forestall – *prevent*

evenly – *calmly*

★ ★ ★ ★ ★ ★ ★ ★ ★ ★

"That's a good long-term plan, but it won't **forestall** the capacity crisis we're facing now."

"What are you saying?" the king asked, dreading his programmer's response.

"I'm saying that we have to write less. At least for now."

The king gasped.

"I know. But it's what we have to do as a galaxy to prevent a capacity catastrophe," the programmer said **evenly**.

"I see," the king said. "Well, thank you for telling me." The king stood up, signalling the end of the meeting. "I'm sure you weren't looking forward to it."

"That's for sure," the programmer said, chuckling with relief. "But I know you'll manage the situation. You always do," he told the king as he walked out. "Let me know if there's anything else I can do to help."

"I will, yes. Thanks again," the king said with a stiff smile.

After he closed the door, the king shook his head and voiced his thoughts. "I can't believe the Gremlin thought I would fall for this. Writing less? Laughable! Like I would ever agree to that. I don't know how he keeps recruiting my programmers, but I'll have to fire him immediately. Too many books. Running out of room. The idea!"

The king put the whole matter out of his head and worked on his upcoming State of the Galaxy speech.

That evening he watched the news with the queen before bed. "Is the galaxy running out of storage space?" the broadcaster asked. "An anonymous source tells Galaxy News that unless drastic cuts are made in our writing production, we won't be able to store new digital books and articles."

The king gasped. "He went to the news?" he said, horrified at the thought.

"Who went to the news?" the queen asked.

"Our programmer. He gave me this ridiculous warning today about some rare metal thing. He said we were nearing storage capacity for digital compositions. Then he had the audacity to suggest we write less," the king scoffed. "He's clearly working for the Gremlin, and I'll be firing him tomorrow."

"Did you say rare metal?" Kirk asked, coming into the room tentatively.

"You're still up, Kirk?" the queen asked.

"Yes, I left my communicator to charge and overheard you as I walked by. What's this about rare metals?"

The king explained what the programmer had said and what was now being reported on the news.

Kirk hesitated but said what he knew his father did not want to hear. "We *are* running out of digital storage capacity. Rare mineral mining is a long-term process. Even if we add new mining companies, we will run out of storage space at our current rate of composition soon."

"You mean...?" the queen began.

"When we're out of space, we'll have to delete books and articles to make room for new ones," Kirk said.

"In the meantime, we have to encourage people to write less, just like our programmer said," the king said sadly.

The three of them were silent for a moment as they pondered a galaxy with less writing.

"Wait!" the queen said, breaking the silence. "What if we don't write less but write more concisely?" she asked.

"Yes, I like where you're going with this. Say more," the king said.

"Using fewer words to communicate clearly is better writing, even when we aren't facing storage limits. I know there's an article about it in the guidebook. We can have the guardians send the information in a mission tomorrow," the queen said.

"And I'll hold a press conference tomorrow, outlining our plan to increase capacity," the king added. "I'll ask all of our adult writers to write using the least number of words to communicate clearly until then."

"Dear, you could have just said that you'd ask our adult writers to be concise," the queen said.

"Indeed," the king said, laughing at himself.

The three of them went to bed, confident that they had a good plan to prevent a crisis.

What does *evenly* mean in the story?

What is concise writing?

Why did the king assume his programmer was working with the Gremlin?

Chapter 32

"I've been asked to be an **ambassador** for Galaxy Jewels!" Ellen told her mother one afternoon.

★ ★ ★ ★ ★ ★ ★ ★ ★

ambassador – *representative*

★ ★ ★ ★ ★ ★ ★ ★ ★

"I haven't heard of them," the queen said.

"They say they're a new company and they need models like me to help grow their brand," Ellen said, bouncing on her toes in excitement. "They will send me free jewelry if I agree to wear it for pictures I share online. They want me to get your permission, of course."

"What if you don't like the jewelry?" the queen asked.

"I get to choose the pieces I like. I looked at their website and the pieces seem to be high quality."

"How are the prices?"

"Mm," Ellen replied, wrinkling her nose, "a little expensive."

"You'll be encouraging your friends to buy expensive jewelry then," the queen warned.

"It's not *that* expensive. And you get what you pay for. Isn't that what you always say?" Ellen countered.

The queen laughed. "Okay. Let me see pictures."

Ellen pulled up the company's website on her communicator.

"Very nice," the queen said. "I like that bracelet a lot."

"You want me to ask if you can be an ambassador, too?" Ellen asked.

The queen laughed. "No. I'll leave that to you. I know you're excited. I'll give you permission to be a jewelry model. Where do I sign?"

"Thanks, Mother!" Ellen said, hugging her.

Ellen was excited to reply to the email and say that she was ready to be a Galaxy Jewels ambassador. When she looked at her inbox, she was surprised to see that she had a second email from the company.

Ellen, do you have friends who would like to get free jewelry, too? Please forward our invitation to them. We would love to have them as part of our team.

Emily **Inveigle**
Ambassador Coordinator for Galaxy Jewelry

Inviting her friends to join her would make it even more fun, Ellen thought. But Ellen replied to the original email first.

★ ★ ★ ★ ★ ★ ★ ★ ★ ★
inveigle – *manipulate*
★ ★ ★ ★ ★ ★ ★ ★ ★ ★

Dear Emily,

I am sooooooooooo excited to say that my mother has given me permission to be an ambassador for you guys. ☺ ☺ ☺ ☺ ☺

Your jewelry is sick! I'm going to attach pictures of the pieces I want to this email. Thank you for sending them to me. I can't wait to get them and take pictures!!!!!!!!!!!!!!

With love ❤,
El English
"All that glitters is not gold."

Ellen kept looking at the pictures of the jewelry she would receive. She couldn't wait to get the pieces! She was considering friends she could forward the email to when she received a reply from the coordinator.

Ellen, we will need to receive a small fee for shipping each piece of jewelry to you. The invoice is attached. When we receive payment, we can process your order.

When you share pictures of yourself wearing our jewelry, we will also need you to have a more professional **persona**. Our ambassadors do not use slang like 'sick,' multiple exclamation points, or childish emojis.

In addition, we will require you to remove the quote from your signature line. While our jewelry isn't gold, it is worthy of kings and queens. Otherwise, we wouldn't have invited you to be an ambassador.

Emily Inveigle
Ambassador Coordinator for Galaxy Jewelry

Ellen's face reddened. She didn't know if she was more angry or embarrassed. Then she checked the invoice total. The company wanted nearly as much for shipping as the jewelry was worth! She was aghast. She would certainly forward the email to her friends but not to recruit them as ambassadors. She would add a note as a warning.

★ ★ ★ ★ ★ ★ ★ ★ ★

persona – *identity*

★ ★ ★ ★ ★ ★ ★ ★ ★

Hey, guys. I was going to ask you to be an ambassador for Galaxy Jewelry with me. They said I would get free jewelry. But look at the invoice they sent me. What a ripoff!!!!!!!!!!!!

Oh yeah. I'm not supposed to use a bunch of exclamation points or emojis either. Emily is a real 🎩. How's that for an emoji? Ha ha. Anyway, tell your friends that being an ambassador for this company is a scam.

Ellen kept checking her email to see her friends' reaction. But her hand flew to her mouth when she saw the first reply. It was from Emily.

Ellen, you obviously didn't intend to send this email to me. While name calling is not a good look for a princess, being slapped with a lawsuit for slander will look even worse. I'll be forwarding your email to our legal department. Unlike you, I know how to forward correctly!

"Oh, no," Ellen said, trembling. "A lawsuit? Father is going to be so upset." She knew she would have to tell her father eventually, but she decided to tell her mother first.

When the queen read through the emails, she sighed.

"I'm sorry," Ellen said tearfully. "Will we have to pay millions of dollars?"

The queen side hugged her daughter in sympathy. "No. The company will not sue a tween girl for an email that wasn't even sent. But the lawsuit threat isn't what I'm concerned about. I'm concerned about the name calling you did."

Ellen nodded humbly. "I know. I'm sorry."

"You're going to have to apologize to her. I know she was rude, but she was also right. Your email *was* unprofessional. I'm going to take some of the blame here, however. I haven't taught you or the boys how to write email for business. We're going to change that right now."

The queen went with Ellen to find the boys and take them to the castle library. There the queen read an article on writing business email from *The Guide to Grammar Galaxy*.

Writing Business Email

Business email should be clear, concise, and professional. Use these tips for saving your reader time and making a good impression.

Keep the email short and make it easy to read. Use a line space between unindented paragraphs. Add bullet points, bold subheadings, and a standard black font to make skimming the email easier.

Use a friendly but professional tone. Greetings like *Dear* and *To whom it may concern* are not used in email. But using a warm or complimentary opening and closing is appropriate. Do not use multiple exclamation points, emojis, or slang. Remove quotes from your signature line.

Make the action required clear. Remind your reader of your desired response at the end of your email using bold type or by adding it to a P.S. Your purpose in writing should also be communicated in the subject line of the email.

Be cautious before sending. Never send an email when angry. Double check the email address for all recipients and make sure all forwards and comments in previous email messages are appropriate. Remember that email can be used in legal cases. Writing truthful, kind emails will maintain your good reputation.

Ellen smacked her forehead with her palm. "Really wish I'd read this before I emailed Emily."

"Who's Emily?" Luke asked.

"Never mind," Ellen and the queen said simultaneously.

"I'd like the three of you to send out a mission on business email right away," the queen said.

They agreed and went to the computer lab to write it.

What is a *persona*?

What did Ellen write in her first email that was unprofessional?

Why does the queen want Ellen to apologize to Emily?

Chapter 33

The king was talking with the Prime Minister in his study. The two had monthly, in-person meetings to discuss the state of the galaxy.

Cook arrived with tea and scones. She liked to deliver the treats herself because the PM (as she called him) was always so complimentary.

"My favorite!" the Prime Minister exclaimed. "And the scones look amazing, too,"

Cook blushed. "Cranberry and walnut," she said, to move his attention to the scones.

"How much does he pay you? I'll double it!" the Prime Minister teased.

Cook just laughed and left the study.

"I may have to limit you to video calls if you're going to try and steal my staff members," the king joked.

The PM laughed and took a bite of scone.

"Now let's discuss bills that are up for consideration in Parliament," the king said.

The PM looked at his notes. "Details and **drivel** mostly. But we do have another bill proposed to end the Guardian Program."

★ ★ ★ ★ ★ ★ ★ ★ ★ ★

drivel – *nonsense*
neophyte – *beginner*
portray – *show*

★ ★ ★ ★ ★ ★ ★ ★ ★ ★

The king groaned. "We know who sponsors this bill every session. But none of the Members are taking it seriously, are they?"

The PM sighed. "Unfortunately, we have some **neophyte** Members who think they can make the news by backing it."

"Who are they? I'll talk to them," the king said, leaning forward to look at the PM's notes.

The PM pulled his tablet into his chest. "I don't think that's a good idea," he said solemnly.

"What? Why not?"

"Honestly? You don't have the influence you once did." When the king raised his eyebrows, he rushed on. "It's not you; it's the Members. They want media attention. If they can **portray** you as a controlling monarch who stands in the way of progress, they will."

"Progress isn't dropping grammar rules," the king said.

"I know your position. But we have Members who disagree."

The king sighed. "What do you propose we do then?"

The PM smiled. "Glad you asked. I was thinking that we need to draw attention to the good work the guardians are doing."

"Yes, and?" the king asked.

"What if the head guardians started a blog?" The PM smiled broadly, proud of his idea.

"A blog. You mean they would regularly write about their work."

"Yes. They already have the Grammar Galaxy Kids website. They would add the blog to it. Kids would read it, which means parents would read it. The value of the Guardian Program would be undeniable."

"That's brilliant. I love the idea! I guess I'll let you meet me here next month, too," he joked.

The king wasted no time sharing the blog idea with Kirk, Luke, and Ellen. He emphasized that it was how they could keep Parliament's support of the Guardian Program.

Ellen was especially enthused. "I love blogs! This is going to be so much fun."

Luke didn't share her enthusiasm. "It's still work," he groaned.

"You'll have to use good grammar and correct spelling. But a blog isn't as formal as a research paper," the king explained.

"I'll ask our programmer to add a blog section to our website," Kirk added.

"I knew I could count on you. I want you to get started this week," the king said.

The following week the PM called the king. "I see that you have the blog up," he observed.

"Yes! The children got right to work. Have you been hearing good things around Parliament already?" he asked with a big smile.

"Uh, no. Their blog isn't anything like what I had in mind."

"What do you mean?" the king asked. He was genuinely surprised but also afraid to hear the PM's answer. He mentally rebuked himself for not checking the blog.

"Well, let's see," the PM said, looking at his tablet. "Here's a post about Ellen's day yesterday. She talked to her friends about whether she should spend money getting her nails done. And here's one by Luke about who will win the Galaxy Series in spaceball."

"Oh," the king said. "I'll take care of it." He didn't want to hear any more from the Prime Minister, so he ended the call abruptly.

As he walked to find his children, he thought of reprimanding them for embarrassing him. But then he stopped. He hadn't taught them how to write a blog post. That was probably because he didn't know how to write one.

When he found them in the media room, he told them what happened and apologized for not giving them the information they needed. He asked Screen to search for tips on writing a good blog post.

"Your Majesty, these tips are from one of the galaxy's top bloggers," Screen said. "First, write a blog post that is about your reader, not you. For example, your reader doesn't care that you had a great lunch yesterday. But your reader is interested in a restaurant recommendation or a new soup recipe. The title of the post should clearly indicate what the reader will get from reading the post. The title "Old-Fashioned Chicken Noodle Soup Recipe" is better than "Lunch with Grandma."

"Second, make your blog post easy to read. Paragraphs should be short. Use subheadings, bullets, and bold text so readers can skim the main points quickly.

"Third, use quality pictures and video that add to the written message. Take these yourself or use media that is legally available for sharing on blogs.

"Fourth, give your reader a call to action. Ask the reader to subscribe to the blog, share the post, or comment."

"These are excellent, Screen. Will you forward these tips to the children's email?" the king asked.

"Certainly, Your Majesty," Screen replied.

"Those tips will help a lot. But writing blog posts like that will take a long time," Ellen said.

"See? That's what I said!" Luke agreed.

"I have an idea," Ellen said, ignoring him. "What if we send out a mission on writing blog posts? We can share the guardians' posts on our website. That's even more proof that the Guardian Program is working. What do you think?" Ellen asked.

"I don't like it," the king said soberly. Then he grinned. "I love it! Get started right away."

What does *drivel* mean?

What should blog posts be about?

Why didn't the king criticize the kids for writing blog posts incorrectly?

Chapter 34

The king was eager to see how Parliament was responding to the guardians' new blog. He called the Prime Minister.

"I know the blog had a rough start, but I'm impressed by the posts our guardians have been writing. Aren't you?" the king asked him on a video call.

"Yes, yes! Much improved over a discussion of spaceball and manicures," the PM joked.

"What are the Members of Parliament saying about it?"

"Positive response overall, but..." the PM began.

"But what?"

"I've heard a few Members say that the guardians are just completing assignments that any student would. We don't need a Guardian Program for this." When the king's face reddened, the PM put his hands up. "Don't kill the messenger!" he said in **mock** fear.

★ ★ ★ ★ ★ ★ ★ ★ ★ ★

mock – *fake*

testimonial – *recommendation*

blurb – *write-up*

★ ★ ★ ★ ★ ★ ★ ★ ★ ★

The king sighed. "Do you have any suggestions then? We can't discontinue the Guardian Program. It works."

"I do have a suggestion. We need to see the human side of the program. What if the blog showed the difference the Guardian Program made in a student's life?"

"Like a **testimonial** from someone in the program?" the king clarified.

"Yes, like that, only not just a **blurb**. I was thinking more like an interview with a guardian."

The king stroked his beard in thought. "So an interview essay shared on the blog. Fantastic idea!"

"Thank you. I have them occasionally," the PM joked.

"I'll let you know when it's published so you can spread the word," the king said.

The king found the children and told them about his conversation with the PM.

"Are you sure the PM isn't working with the Gremlin?" Luke joked. "Another writing assignment," he groaned.

"We learned a little bit about interviewing when we wrote profile essays, but I would like to know best practices for writing an interview essay. We'll read the guidebook before we start," Kirk told his father.

"I'm impressed, Kirk. Thank you for taking the lead on this. I knew I could count on you," the king said.

Later, Kirk read the article on interview essays from *The Guide to Grammar Galaxy* aloud.

Interview Essays

Journalists often write interview essays. The articles rely on people as sources rather than media. Interviewees may be single or multiple experts, participants, or celebrities. Follow these steps to write an interview essay:

Decide on the purpose of the essay. Is it educational, persuasive, or entertaining? Your purpose will guide you in choosing people to interview.

Research the subject. You must be familiar with the key facts, arguments, or life events before you set up an interview. To prepare, read a book, some primary articles, and another interview essay if available. You may find the names of people you could interview in these resources. A database of experts willing to speak with journalists is another resource to check.

Use your research to make a list of questions for your interviewee(s). Questions should be open-ended, not prompting a yes-or-no answer. You will ask the questions your reader likely has to get the interviewee's opinion, clarification, or experience. Have more questions than you need, allowing time to focus on the most interesting topics.

Schedule and complete the interview. Let the interviewee know if you'll be talking in person, in a virtual meeting, or on the phone. Give the time required to complete the interview and where the completed essay will be published.

Be on time and ready to record responses in writing and via recording. Ask easy questions about the interviewee's education, experience, or family to begin. Smile

---

and nod encouragingly while the interviewee is speaking. Wait to ask another question until the answer is complete.

When you have finished, thank the interviewee for their time. Make sure you have their contact information so you can send the essay in draft for their review.

Choose a format for the essay. A narrative interview essay tells a story from your perspective or from your interviewee's. Quotes may be included to enhance the story.

A question-and-answer format begins with an introduction that explains the purpose of the interview. The body of the essay includes the questions in bold type followed by the interviewee's responses. Quotes do not have to be given in their entirety but should not be edited to change the interviewee's meaning. The conclusion may include your reaction to the interview, resources for more information, and/or the interviewee's future plans.

Title, edit, and proofread the essay. The title should clearly communicate the subject of the essay and entice your target audience to read it. Read the essay aloud to look for clunky sentences that need to be rewritten. Double-check any statistics, quotes, or sources for accuracy. Use a program to check for spelling and grammar errors. Ask someone else to review your essay. Send your interviewee a copy of the essay for review. Give a deadline by which you need to receive their approval.

"But for our interview essay, we just have to find a guardian to interview, right?" Luke asked.

"Right. And our purpose is to convince Parliament to keep the Guardian Program in place," Kirk answered.

"I know the perfect guardian for us to interview!" Ellen exclaimed.

"Great! Get the interview set up. I'd like to get this published as soon as possible," Kirk said.

A few weeks later, the king spoke with the Prime Minister again. "What's the word on the interview essay the children published? I reviewed it and thought it was excellent," the king said.

"I agree. Well done essay. The young lady they interviewed loves being a guardian," the PM said.

"I hear a 'but' coming."

"*But* some of the Members have said that this guardian is a friend of Ellen's. Of course she is enthusiastic about the program." The Prime Minister looked sorry he had to disappoint the king.

"I see," the king said, tenting his hands in thought. The two sat in silence for a few moments. Then the king smiled. "What if we publish lots of guardian interviews?"

"I see where you're going with this, but how would your children have time for it?" the PM asked.

"Leave that to me," the king said. He ended the call and went to find his children.

When the king had gathered his children in the library, he explained the problem and suggested they send out a mission to solve it. "So the guardians are going to interview other guardians?" Ellen asked.

"No. You're going to send them the questions and they will interview themselves and write up the essays. You'll publish them on the blog," the king explained.

"Brilliant," Kirk said, smiling.

What is a blurb?

What are two formats for an interview essay?

Why is the king interested in publishing lots of guardian interviews?

Chapter 35

"Is Parliament convinced that the Guardian Program is worth continuing?" Kirk asked his father during a break from their tennis practice.

"I don't see how they couldn't be. We have so many **endorsements** of the program," the king said.

★ ★ ★ ★ ★ ★ ★ ★ ★ ★

endorsements – *commendations*

★ ★ ★ ★ ★ ★ ★ ★ ★ ★

Kirk didn't seem convinced as he dribbled a tennis ball with his racket. "The guardians are the Gremlin's enemy. He won't give up trying to shut us down," he said soberly.

"Well, in this case, I hope you're wrong, Kirk. Let's work on serves, and I'll talk to the Prime Minister later today," the king said.

The king was in a **chipper** mood when the Prime Minister took his call. "Have you seen all those glowing reviews? When was the last time young people were so positive about learning language arts?" the king asked him.

★ ★ ★ ★ ★ ★ ★ ★ ★ ★

chipper – *cheerful*

prodigious – *impressive*

★ ★ ★ ★ ★ ★ ★ ★ ★ ★

"Yes, they're **prodigious** to be sure. The kids seem to love the program..."

"Why do I think there's another 'but' coming?" the king said peevishly.

"But...there are still Members of Parliament who are unimpressed."

"What would impress them? Good grammar, I'm tiring of these people," the king groused.

"I have an idea," the PM responded eagerly. "My wife has been listening to podcasts. She loves them! She'll make me listen to her favorite episodes," he said, chuckling. "Anyway, what if the guardians started a podcast?"

"You don't think that's too much for them, do you? Blogging and podcasting on top of running the Guardian Program?" the king asked sarcastically.

"Oh, my apologies. They do have a lot of responsibilities." The PM hesitated and watched the king thinking about it.

"I'll have to get back to you," the king grumbled, ending the call without the normal farewell.

At dinner that evening, the queen could tell something was wrong. "What has the Gremlin done this time?" she asked.

"Nothing yet," the king sighed.

"Did you talk with the Prime Minister about the interviews?" Kirk asked.

"I did." He shook his head. "It hasn't changed the minds of the Members who are determined to shut down the Guardian Program. But he had the crazy idea that you three could start a podcast to have more influence," he said with a chuckle.

"A podcast? I love podcasts!" the queen enthused.

"Me too!" Ellen added.

"I enjoy them as well," Kirk said.

159

"Let me guess. Now we're making a podcast. I have no idea how to do that," Luke said.

"Is it something you'd like to do?" the king asked Kirk and Ellen. Ellen nodded enthusiastically.

Kirk said, "I would want logical steps to follow, of course." The rest of the family laughed.

"Well, it would be a good learning experience for you three. Screen," the king commanded, "would you give us some tips for podcasting?"

Screen replied, "Your Majesty, these tips are from one of the galaxy's top podcasters. First, choose a topic you are passionate about and a show name that will appeal to an audience. As host, you should be relatable with a unique style."

"Right! I listen to a podcaster who used to have too much stuff. I can relate to that," the queen said. "She calls herself the clutter fairy, which is certainly unique."

"Second, decide the format for the podcast. Will it be a solo, interview, or co-hosted format? You will prepare a script for the episode based on the format. The episode can be written out and read in a conversational tone. Or it can be outlined, allowing the host or co-hosts to speak casually. Every episode includes an introduction of the host and what the listener can expect from the episode. If the episode is an interview, the guest is introduced.

"The conclusion of the episode should be a summary of what was discussed with a call-to-action or what you'd like the audience to do after listening," Screen said.

"Send us money!" Luke joked.

"What about music?" Ellen asked, ignoring him.

"Music is usually used to introduce and conclude a podcast. It is also used to indicate the beginning and end of advertisements in the show. The music should fit the tone and intended audience," Screen said.

"We could interview a guardian for the podcast," Ellen said, thinking aloud.

"That's a great idea!" Kirk replied.

"It might make them nervous," Luke warned.

"That's true," Kirk said. "What if we sent the guardians a mission on podcasting? We can get some tips from Screen on being a good podcast guest."

160

"Maybe some guardians would be inspired to start their own shows. That would impress Parliament for sure," Ellen said.

"You three never cease to amaze me. The galaxy is in good hands," the king said, feeling emotional.

After dinner, Kirk, Luke, and Ellen worked with Screen to create a mission on podcasting.

What does *prodigious* mean?

What is a call-to-action?

Why is it important to choose a podcast topic you're passionate about?

Chapter 36

"Our podcast is the top new show in education!" Ellen announced to her family in the sunroom.

"That's wonderful!" the queen replied.

"Hey!" Luke said, clapping.

Comet started barking at all the excitement.

"He's congratulating us," Luke joked.

"Now Parliament has to be convinced that the Guardian Program is essential," Kirk said.

"I'd like to think so," the king said.

"But you're not sure," Kirk said, speaking for him.

"Right. I have a call scheduled with the Prime Minister today. I'm hoping for the best but preparing for the worst."

"But right now we need to celebrate," Ellen said, beaming. "I've never been a top podcaster before."

"I couldn't help but overhear," Cook said, coming into the sunroom. "I'm going to make a special celebration meal."

"I'll help!" Ellen said.

"I'll help, too," the queen added.

"Uh, that's okay," Cook said. "It's my treat."

"In other words, we just make more work for you," the queen teased.

"Uhh," Cook stammered.

"That's a yes," Luke joked. Everyone laughed.

The king could tell by the look on the Prime Minister's face that the attitude toward the Guardian Program hadn't changed. "It's coming up for debate later this week," he said.

"What is?" the king asked.

"A bill that would effectively end the Guardian Program," the PM said with **measured** emotion.

"They can't do that!" the king cried.

"They can, my friend. It's wrong, but they can." His eyes glistened as he watched the king absorb the news.

★ ★ ★ ★ ★ ★ ★ ★ ★

measured – *restrained*
disposition – *nature*
outdone – *bested*

★ ★ ★ ★ ★ ★ ★ ★ ★

"There must be something we can do," the king said, staring out his study window. "Wait! They allow speakers who aren't Members to address Parliament about bills that can affect them."

"Right, but you know you can't speak—" the PM began.

"Not me, Kirk. He would speak on behalf of the guardians," the king interjected. He watched the Prime Minister, willing him to agree.

"I would have to get the Leader to approve."

"Do it!" the king said.

"All right. But there is no guarantee that Kirk will stop them from dismantling the program."

"I know. But we have to try," the king said.

The king worked at having a cheerful **disposition** for the celebration dinner. The queen noticed but decided to play along for the children's sake.

"Cook, you've **outdone** yourself!" she said as she and the staff served the meal. "This looks incredible."

"I wanted a special meal for the famous podcasters," she said, ruffling Luke's hair.

"He didn't do that much," Ellen said to correct Cook.

"I told you when you had a bad idea. I saved you plenty of times," Luke said lightheartedly. Cook and the family laughed.

The king decided to enjoy himself and worry about the bill before Parliament later.

But he didn't have to approach Kirk. After dinner, Kirk talked with his parents in the media room. "They still want to discontinue the Guardian Program, don't they?"

The king nodded solemnly.

"It's not your fault, Kirk. You and your siblings have done an incredible job with the young people in this galaxy," the queen said.

"But there must be something we can do," Kirk said.

"There is. At this point the Members who are on the Gremlin's side have a lot of influence. But if you address Parliament with a persuasive speech, there's still a chance we can save the program," the king said.

"Just me?" Kirk asked.

"Yes. I'll help you prepare, starting tomorrow. That is if you're willing," the king said.

"Let's prepare now," Kirk said. He had a determined look that the queen had never seen before.

"Are you sure? It's late," the king said.

"I'm sure. But I think we need more than just my speech to save the program. We need every guardian to deliver a persuasive speech."

The king was astonished. "You're right, Kirk. We should send out an emergency mission with a reminder of how to deliver an effective persuasive speech—getting the audience's attention, explaining why the issue matters to them, and encouraging action or a new attitude about the Guardian Program. The guardians can give the speeches on video online or locally in their Grammar Girls and Guys groups."

The king went with Kirk to find Luke and Ellen and explain the situation. They agreed to begin work on a persuasive speaking mission immediately.

What does *disposition* mean?

What three steps to writing a persuasive speech did the king mention?

How did Kirk know the Guardian Program was still being threatened?

About the Author

Dr. Melanie Wilson was a clinical psychologist working in a Christian practice, a college instructor, freelance writer, and public speaker before she felt called to stay home and educate her children. She is a mother of six and has homeschooled for more than 20 years. She says it's her most fulfilling vocation.

Melanie has always been passionate about language arts and used bits and pieces of different curriculum and approaches to teach her children and friends' children. In 2014, she believed she had another calling to write the curriculum she'd always wanted as a homeschooling mom — one that didn't take a lot of time, made concepts simple and memorable, and was enough fun to keep her kids motivated.

Books have been a family business since the beginning. Melanie's husband Mark has been selling library books for since graduating from college. Melanie and the kids frequently pitch in to help at the annual librarians' conference. Grammar Galaxy is another family business that has been a great learning opportunity for their children.

When Melanie isn't busy homeschooling, visiting her kids in college, or writing, she loves to play tennis with family and friends.

Melanie is also the author of *The Organized Homeschool Life* and *A Year of Living Productively*. Learn more at HomeschoolSanity.com and FunToLearnBooks.com.

About the Illustrator

Rebecca Mueller has had an interest in drawing from an early age. Rebecca quickly developed a unique style and illustrated her first books, a short series of bedtime stories with her mother, at age 9. Rebecca graduated with a BA in English from the University of Missouri - St. Louis with a minor in Studio Art and her Master of Library and Information Science at the University of Missouri – Columbia. She currently works as a Youth Specialist at the St. Louis Public Library.

Appendix: Answers to Comprehension Questions

Chapter 1
What does *egregious* mean? outrageous

What is censorship? when an authority eliminates, punishes, or hides communication it does not approve of.

Why would the Gremlin want to shut down *The Groaner*? It was making fun of him, too.

Chapter 2
What does *unwitting* mean? unknowing

What is an ad hominem attack? criticisms of the person or group that aren't relevant to the issue

Who is the most likely backer of the Citizen Fact-Checkers? The Gremlin

Chapter 3
What does *obliterate* mean? destroy

What are some hands-on activities for remembering science information? Complete an experiment, build a model, or sketch the process

Why didn't Ellen tell her father the real reason for her plan? She didn't think he would take action to prevent a catastrophe.

Chapter 4
What does *pressing* mean in the story? urgent

Themes are the author's _____ on common subjects. opinion

What is the theme for the books on the Librarians' Choice for Children book list? anti-monarchy

Chapter 5
What does *obscured* mean? hidden

What are symbolic plots called? allegories

Why did the king think *Dark Winter* was anti-monarchy? The king is described as a tyrant.

Chapter 6
What does *listlessly* mean? lethargically

Which aspects of literature are used to create mood? The setting, illustrations, and vocabulary

Why didn't the children respond well to their mother's morning greeting? The galaxy's tone and mood of the month are angry and hopeless

Chapter 7
What does *debase* mean? shame

Which point of view is the least common? 2nd person

Why were the diary and the mystery novel different? Their point of view had been changed.

Chapter 8
What does *menacing* mean? ominous

Why do authors use flashback? explain events and characters' behavior

Why did the music play when the king asked about History Month? It was foreshadowing of the connection to the problem.

Chapter 9
What does *intervened* mean? interfered

Why are movies literature? They include the same literary concepts that are studied in written works.

What was the king's attitude toward movies at first? He didn't think they were as worthwhile as books.

Chapter 10
What does *capacious* mean? spacious

What is a phonetic dictionary? a dictionary that gives the spelling of words based on their sound

Why wasn't Luke enjoying Science Camp? He wasn't allowed to dictate and was embarrassed by his spelling.

Chapter 11
What does *inane* mean? silly

How do the French usually spell \sh\? ch

Why was the king so upset about the spelling rules? The basis for them was incorrect and he wanted his kids to avoid the hassle.

Chapter 12
What does *composure* mean? self-control

What should be done with numbers in dialogue or quotes? should generally be spelled out

Why was the queen surprised that Ellen wanted to talk to her father? Ellen normally talked to her when she was upset

Chapter 13
What does *impishly* mean? mischievously

How are hyphens used? To connect compound words and adjectives and when words are divided at the end of a line

Why were the king and queen in conflict? The queen wanted to focus on family and the king couldn't stop thinking about hyphens.

Chapter 14
What does *histrionics* mean? dramatics

What is the difference between *emigrate* and *immigrate*? leave country vs. come to country

What should the queen have said instead of: "I want to ensure you that bidding on any of these items promotes reading"? I want to assure you that bidding on any of these items promotes reading.

Chapter 15
What does *resuscitate* mean? save

What is medical jargon? terms medical professionals know and the rest of us don't

Why was Grandpa George getting upset with the nurse? She didn't understand him.

Chapter 16
What does *cavalier* mean? inconsiderate

What is an idiom? an expression that means something other than its words indicate

Why were idioms being literally experienced? They had been moved to Nonfiction Province.

Chapter 17
What does *incorrigible* mean in the story? beastly

What is required to have shades of meaning? synonyms

Why does the queen want to wait to talk to Ellen? Ellen won't be able to communicate well without shades of meaning.

Chapter 18
What does *fallacy* mean? error

What do word analogies test? logical reasoning as applied to vocabulary

Why did Kirk fail the analogies test? He was expecting a test of logical fallacies and when he was wrong, he gave up, assuming he would fail.

Chapter 19
What does *imperious* mean? arrogant

What is an object pronoun that wasn't in custody? you, it, me, him, her

Why was the king relieved when the queen left his study? She was using incorrect grammar.

Chapter 20
What does *prevail* mean? triumph

What are the demonstrative pronouns? this, that, these, and those

Why can't indefinite pronouns replace subject pronouns? Subject pronouns replace specific nouns whereas indefinite pronouns are not specific and may not be singular or plural as required.

Chapter 21
What does *exultant* mean? joyful

What is the progressive tense? Verb tense that shows the action is in progress and ongoing

Why didn't the editor want the progressive tense in *The Guardian*? He didn't want to show agreement with liberal politics.

Chapter 22
What does *constraining* mean? limiting

What are the five grammatical moods? interrogative, indicative, imperative, conditional, subjunctive

Why was the queen angry about the king's concerns about Mel Wright? At first because she felt the king was thinking the worst without evidence, but also because she had the same concern that she hadn't admitted to herself.

Chapter 23
What does *dispassionate* mean? unemotional

What part of speech is the word pair *to be*? infinitive

Why was Ellen able to say *cook, play,* and *read*? because they aren't infinitives or participles

Chapter 24
What does *ostentatiously* mean? showily

What is an independent clause? Includes a subject, verb, and a complete thought

Why shouldn't all clauses be independent? Sentences wouldn't make sense.

<u>Chapter 25</u>
What does *gall* mean? nerve

What is a misplaced modifier? words, phrases, or clauses that are separated from the word they explain, resulting in an uncertain meaning

What did Cook mean to say? "I have some hot apple pie in the kitchen for Your Majesty."

<u>Chapter 26</u>
What does *appropriation* mean? stealing

When are semicolons particularly important? in a list of items containing commas

How did the *Punctuation Appropriation* documentary try to change opinions? Using music and video to evoke emotion and compassion.

<u>Chapter 27</u>
What does *pivotal* mean? decisive

What is parallel structure? using the same grammatical composition in a sentence.

What should the king have said he wanted for breakfast, using parallel structure? eggs, bacon, and fresh fruit

<u>Chapter 28</u>
What does *plethora* mean? overabundance

What is possibility thinking? brainstorming or generating many ideas without criticism.

Why didn't the king want to mention writer's block to the media? He doesn't want people to panic.

Chapter 29
What does *iterative* mean? continual

Why should sentence starters vary? To prevent sentences from sounding repetitive and robotic.

Why did Luke think Kirk sounded like a robot? He began all his sentences with *the*.

Chapter 30
What does *pointedly* mean in the story? sharply

What is a verb that is never in passive voice? Verbs that cannot have direct objects like arrive, come, die, go, live, sleep.

How would "My ways have to be changed" be written in active voice? I have to change my ways.

Chapter 31
What does *evenly* mean in the story? calmly

What is concise writing? Using fewer words to communicate clearly.

Why did the king assume his programmer was working with the Gremlin? Because he suggested writing less, just as the Gremlin would. A previous programmer had worked for the Gremlin.

Chapter 32
What is a *persona*? identity

What did Ellen write in her first email that was unprofessional? Slang, emojis, multiple exclamation points, and a signature quote.

Why does the queen want Ellen to apologize to Emily? Because her name calling was wrong, even though Emily was rude.

Chapter 33
What does _drivel_ mean? nonsense

What should blog posts be about? the reader, not the writer

Why didn't the king criticize the kids for writing blog posts incorrectly? He hadn't instructed them in writing good blog posts.

Chapter 34
What is a blurb? write-up

What are two formats for an interview essay? narrative and question-and-answer

Why is the king interested in publishing lots of guardian interviews? to impress Parliament with the success of the Guardian Program

Chapter 35
What does _prodigious_ mean? impressive

What is a call-to-action? The action you want the audience to take after listening.

Why is it important to choose a podcast topic you're passionate about? So you don't lose interest in it over time and so you are more interesting to listen to.

Chapter 36
What does _disposition_ mean? nature

What three steps to writing a persuasive speech did the king mention? getting the audience's attention, explaining why the issue matters to them, and encouraging action or a new attitude

How did Kirk know the Guardian Program was still being threatened? He saw his father's expression at dinner.

Made in the USA
Columbia, SC
27 June 2022

62369736R00096